Signs & Seasons

Field Journal and Test Manual

Fourth Day Press
Cleveland, Ohio, USA

❀❀❀ Anno Domini MMVIII ❀❀❀

Signs & Seasons
Field Journal and Test Manual

© 2008 Jay Ryan
(Minor Revisions - © 2010 Jay Ryan)

Original illustrations created by the author © 2008 Jay Ryan

International Standard Book Number: 978-0-9792211-1-8

Fourth Day Press
Cleveland, Ohio
www.ClassicalAstronomy.com

And God said, Let there bee lights in the firmament of the heauen, to diuide the day from the night: and let them be for signes and for seasons, and for dayes and yeeres. And let them be for lights in the firmament of the heauen, to giue light vpon the earth: and it was so. And God made two great lights: the greater light to rule the day, and the lesser light to rule the night: he made the starres also. And God set them in the firmament of the heauen, to giue light vpon the earth: And to rule ouer the day, and ouer the night, and to diuide the light from the darkenes: and God saw that it was good. And the euening and the morning were the fourth day. — Genesis 1: 14-19

Author's Note:

This field journal has been created in response to many requests from parents for chapter tests so that a grade could be assigned to their highschool students. Also, since *Signs & Seasons* is a "lab" course, this field journal is intended to encourage students to perform the Field Activities and thereby learn the sky through observation. The tables and project layouts in this workbook are designed to help students organize information and tabulate data, and thus make a good start toward observing the sky.

Table of Contents

Test Manual

A series of tests are presented for each chapter of Signs & Seasons, to measure a student's understanding of the subject matter and enable a course grade to be assigned

Instructions

As with many things in life, we learn by doing, and visual astronomy is no exception. One could read *Signs & Seasons* and perhaps understand the concepts *in theory*, but without actually observing the sky, one would never master the subject *in practice*. One can only get a limited understanding from reading *Signs & Seasons*, since it shows flat pictures, unlike the real sky which is three-dimensional and visible in all directions. *Signs & Seasons* is therefore most useful as an instruction guide for beginning to learn to observe the sky.

As stated over a century ago by noted astronomer Asaph Hall (quoted in the introduction to *Signs & Seasons*):

Elementary astronomy should be taught in the high schools and preparatory schools, as well as in the colleges. Preparatory work in it ought to be accepted for admission to college.

The field activities in this booklet are intended to assist high school homeschoolers in recording work hours of "lab" coursework that will establish high school credit for transcript records. However, these activities can also be adapted as "unit study" work for younger students under parent's supervision.

Field Journal Section

Your field journal allows you to record observations, including the *time and date*, and also the *amount of time* spent on each activity. You can write directly into your field journal or use it as a guide to creating a separate field journal in which you can create your own tables and arrange pages as you desire, and perhaps insert the pages into a three-ring binder.

Rising and Setting of the Sun and Moon

Many activities require finding the times of sunrise and sunset and also moonrise and moonset. This information can usually be found in your local newspaper, an almanac, or from many sites on the Internet. One handy web site for finding this data is:

The U.S. Naval Observatory *Complete Sun and Moon Data for One Day* web site

http://aa.usno.navy.mil/data/docs/RS_OneDay.html

Types of Field Activities

* *Observation Activities* - many activities entail direct observation of the sky and recording the results in the field journal. Handy tables are provided for each chapter throughout this journal for recording your observations.

* *Sketching Activities* - in some activities, sketches will be made of the Sun, Moon and stars. Sketching requires close examination of the illustrations in *Signs & Seasons*, and reinforces a deeper visual comprehension of the subject matter. Don't worry if you're not the greatest artist! Your field journal is mainly your own tool for learning the sky.

* *Manipulative Activities* - some "hands-on" activities require the use of a typical rotating 12-inch world globe. If you don't own one, these are often found at public libraries. Also, some activities involve creating *volvelles,* traditional paper instruments for depicting the motions in the sky. A Volvelle Section is included for these activities.

Completion of the Field Activities

These field activities should be self-guided. Try to do most of the activities, but do not worry if you can't complete them all. Some activities involve observing certain constellations, but not all are visible at every month of the year. Also, sky observation requires clear skies, which are not always available in every climate during every season of the year. Therefore, these activities can only be performed as opportunity permits. For these reasons, this course does not fit inro a tidy week-by-week lesson plan.

In the event of persistently cloudy or rainy weather in your area, you can use a planetarium software program to simulate the sky and perform "virtual" sky observations. One such program is *Stellarium*, an open source planetarium astronomy application available for free download at *http://www.stellarium.org*.

Please note - all the field activities from each chapter should be started and worked on concurrently. Most activities entail tabulating data collected over the span of weeks and months. Start new chapters while still working on earlier chapters, in order to finish the program within a year.

Expand your study beyond *Signs & Seasons*. For example, you can learn more constellations and study the sky with a telescope. Or you can become a member of a local planetarium, observatory or astronomy club. A list of these local organizations can be found at *http://skyandtelescope.com*. The more you study the sky, the more you will learn and understand.

Test Manual Section

This workbook also includes a section of tests for each chapter of *Signs & Seasons*. In this way, progress and understanding of the subject matter can be measured and a grade can be assigned for highschoolers in jurisdictions in which a grade is required. Since direct observation of the sky is the goal of *Signs & Seasons*, many illustrations are included so as to test the student on the appearances of the sky.

Timekeeping for High School Credit

The field activities in *Signs & Seasons* are elective and students can do as many or as few as they like. More hours can be earned with the completion of a greater number of activities, and thus more credit can be achieved. The field activities in this workbook are more than sufficient in number and complexity to allow a student to document 120 hours of "lab work" corresponding to one full high school credit according to the standard "Carnegie Unit" of 120 hours equalling one credit for a high school course (and 60 hours for a half-credit, and 30 hours for a quarter-credit, etc.).

Using the Signs & Seasons Field Activity Timesheets

In order to establish work hours for high school credit, use these tables to record the time spent working on the field activities. Record all of the time taken for this course, including reading the *Signs & Seasons* curriculum, performing the hands-on activities, observing the sky, recording observations in the field journal, analyzing data, taking tests, and visiting a local planetarium, observatory, and astronomy club.

Three timesheet pages are attached, enough to record 300 activity sessions. While this should be more than adequate, copies of these pages can be made if more space is required. The timesheets include spaces to record the activity, the date the activity was performed, start and end times for each session, and total time spent on that session. The activity can be identified as a simple abbreviation, such as "Ch. 1, twilight" or whatever works to help you remember what you did.

To simplify timekeeping, record your time in increments of 0.1 hours (six minutes). For example, if you're outdoors observing and recording for a half hour, write down 0.5 hrs; if you're working on a hands-on activity for an hour and 12 minutes, write down 1.2 hrs. Just be sure to pay attention to your starting and ending times so as to make an accurate record.

When you reach the bottom of a column, add the total hours recorded in that column. When you complete another column, add the total hours of that column to the grand total of the previous column, thus keeping a running total of hours spent on the field activities.

Signs & Seasons Field Activity Timesheet

(Sheet # ____)

Activity	Date	Start	End	Total		Activity	Date	Start	End	Total
				5						
				10						
				15						
				20						
				25						
				30						
				35						
				40						
				45						
				50						
		Total This Column						Total This Column		
		Grand Total						Grand Total		

Signs & Seasons Field Activity Timesheet

Activity	Date	Start	End	Total		Activity	Date	Start	End	Total
					5					
					10					
					15					
					20					
					25					
					30					
					35					
					40					
					45					
					50					
			Total This Column						Total This Column	
			Grand Total						Grand Total	

Signs & Seasons Field Activity Timesheet

(Sheet # ____)

Activity	Date	Start	End	Total		Activity	Date	Start	End	Total
					5					
					10					
					15					
					20					
					25					
					30					
					35					
					40					
					45					
					50					
		Total This Column						Total This Column		
		Grand Total						Grand Total		

Field Journal

Mastering Your Knowledge and Understanding of the Sky through Practical Observation

It is the glory of God to conceal a thing: but the honour of kings is to search out a matter. –Proverbs 25:2

 Signs & Seasons

Field Activities for Chapter 1
The Light He Called Day

Create a Backyard Compass

Necessary materials:
Some sticks, a tape measure, and five paving stones from a garden supply center.

This is a very important project that will be used throughout the field activities. You will make a compass that is big enough to stand on, as shown in the book. This will help you find direction and learn to orient yourself as you learn the constellations and signs of the seasons.

The first thing you need to do is find "high noon," when the Sun is highest in the sky and the shadows are the shortest. As Pliny the Elder instructed in A.D. 50:

After observing the quarter in which the Sun rises on any given day, at the sixth hour of the day (i.e. at Noon) take your position in such a manner as to have the point of the Sun's rising on your left; you will then have the south directly facing you, and the north at your back: a line drawn through a field in this direction is called the "cardinal" line... It will be the sixth hour of the day, at the moment when the shadow straight before him is the shortest. Through the middle of this shadow, taken lengthwise, a furrow must be traced in the ground with a hoe, or else a line drawn with ashes, some twenty feet in length.

So here's what to do:

*   Pick a site in your backyard away from the house and other buildings, with a wide open view in as many directions as possible. (Get your parent's permission before beginning!)

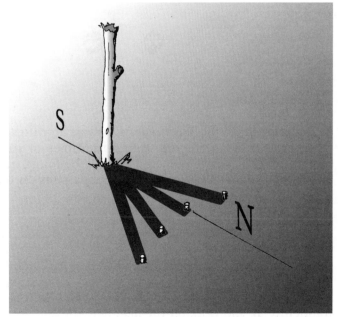

*   Place a stick in the ground about one foot long. Be sure the stick is placed very straight in the ground.

*   On a sunny day, observe the shadows from between about 11:00 AM and 2:00 PM (since high noon can occur at very different times depending on the season and your location.)

*   Every 20-30 minutes, place a short twig into the ground at the end of the stick's shadow.

*   After the time is up, use a ruler or tape measure to find the distance between each twig and the stick. The shortest distance is your *cardinal line* that runs from north to south!

*   Carefully extend your cardinal line 10 feet (3 meters) to the north and to the south from your stick. Place paving stones at each point. These are the north and south points of your compass.

*   Remove the stick and place a paving stone in its place. This is your central *standing stone*.

*   From your standing stone, measure a line perpendicular to your cardinal line, another 10 feet (3 meters) on either side. Check carefully to make sure your lines are even. Place paving stones at these ends. These are the east and west points of your compass.

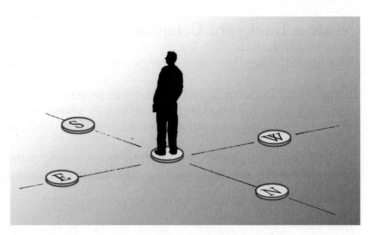

*   Recheck your compass over the next two or three days to make sure that the shadows really are shortest in the direction of your cardinal line.

*   When your compass is accurate, you can now stand on your standing stone and look at each direction of the compass, day or night and when it's cloudy!

*   You can write the names of the directions on your compass points -- N-E-W-S – help every member of the family find the compass points. Also, you can dig out under your stones to set them in the earth, to make sure the lawn mower won't hit them.

*   If space does not permit, you can create a temporary backyard compass on a driveway or other pavement surface using sidewalk chalk.

❁   ❁   ❁   ❁   ❁

Please Note!

As mentioned in the instructions, many activities in this workbook, beginning with these in Chapter 1, will require you to find the times of sunrise and sunset, along with moonrise and moonset. This information can usually be found in your local newspaper, an almanac such as *The Old Farmer's Almanac*, or from many sites on the Internet. One handy web site for finding this data is:

The U.S. Naval Observatory *Complete Sun and Moon Data for One Day* web site

http://aa.usno.navy.mil/data/docs/RS_OneDay.html

It is recommended that you bookmark this web page on your internet browser and refer to it frequently as you work on the field activities.

Sunrise, Sunset and Noon

While standing in your backyard compass, observe sunrise, noon, and sunset once a week over a span of ten weeks. Sketch the views of the Sun you observe, indicating the directions and including a horizon with a treeline and/or buildings. Include the date and times of sunrise and sunset as found in your local newspaper, almanac, or from the Internet.

Date					
Sunrise					
Noon					
Sunset					

Date					
Sunrise					
Noon					
Sunset					

Noon shadows

Draw a sketch of your shadow showing its direction in your backyard compass at 12:00 PM on the clock. Record the clock time at "high noon," when your shadow points toward the north. (Indicate whether it is Daylight Savings Time.) Repeat these measurements at least once a week for a period of three months. Record the time difference between "clock noon" and "high noon" over the months.

Date					
Sketch 12:00P.M					
High Noon					
Time Difference					

Date					
Sketch 12:00P.M					
High Noon					
Time Difference					

Date					
Sketch 12:00P.M					
High Noon					
Time Difference					

Is your neighborhood "astronomically aligned"?

Look at a map of your community and find the compass on the map. Are the streets in your community laid out to follow the compass directions? Confirm the map with your own observations. Stand on your sidewalk or driveway around the time of "high noon," when the shadows are shortest. Measure your own shadow or the shadow of a family member to find when the shadows are shortest. Do the shortest shadows line up with your driveway or sidewalk? If so, you can make a "backyard compass" on your driveway with sidewalk chalk!

Compare the times of your shortest shadows between your driveway or sidewalk and your backyard compass. Are they the same? (If not, one or the other is wrong!)

Walk around your neighborhood around sunrise, noon and sunset. List any "astronomically aligned" streets in your community, especially ones that have clear views of the horizon.

Streets that Run North and South		*Streets that Run East and West*	

Draw a map of your neighborhood and include a compass to indicate direction. Include the streets listed above and indicate them with a colored highlighter.

Exposures

Record the rooms in your home that receive the Sun in the morning, noon, and evening, and also any rooms into which the noon Sun never directly shines.

Morning Sun	*Noon Sun*	*Evening Sun*	*No Noon Sun*

List some outdoor plants at your house that enjoy the following sunlight conditions.

Partial Sunlight	*Full Sunlight*	*Shade Plants*

Draw an overhead view of your house and yard. Indicate the directional orientation of the house as compared with your backyard compass. Show the indoor rooms for one level and also the outdoor plants as listed above. Indicate the exposures for each side of the house.

Finding Direction Around Your Hometown

As you travel with family to stores and other places, note the time of day and the direction of the Sun. Track your direction based on the Sun's position at that time. Note how your direction of travel changes with left and right turns. When you arrive at your destination, determine which general directions you traveled from home, *e.g.* southeast, northwest, *etc.* When you get home, confirm this with a map of your community. Learn the general directions to at least 10 familiar places. Include the nearest town, your regular shopping center, your church, grandparents' house, three neighbors (in different directions), and/or three friends (in different directions). Note the exposures of the front entrances.

Location	General Direction from Home	Exposure of Front Entrance

Draw a map of your community showing your home and the locations listed above. Include a compass and show the general directions to the locations listed above.

Twilight Activity

As day changes to night, there are changes in our eyes' ability to see color. The retinas in our eyes include rods and cones. During the bright daylight, our cones help us see color, and also to read words on paper. At night, our rods help us see in darkness, but the rods cannot distinguish color or enable us to read.

For this activity, plan on staying outside the whole time as night falls. Avoid outdoor lighting since this will affect your perception of the twilight. Sit in a comfortable chair, maybe on a deck or patio. Do this activity with a friend or family member or while listening to music so that you can pass the time as darkness falls. Be sure to dress appropriately and keep some bug spray handy!

Record the time of sunset, either by observation or from a time found in the newspaper or on the Internet. During early twilight, note the bright colors in the sky and with ground objects. Keep some reading matter and a variety of different colored objects with you. As twilight deepens, record the times when it becomes difficult to read, and also when it becomes difficult to distinguish colors. At the same time, record the times when the first stars can be seen. Record a later time when you notice several stars that can be seen. Record a time when the sky begins to look starry, but a patch of twilight glow can still be seen on the sunset horizon. Finally, record a time when no twilight can be seen. How do the times of the stages of twilight compare with the changes from day vision to night vision?

Repeat this activity to collect a data set over a span of weeks. Note any variations in the times.

Date				
Time of Sunset				
Hard to Read				
Hard to Tell Colors				
First Stars Visible				
Sky Looks Starry				
No More Twilight				
Notes				

Earth's Rotation

Sketch a picture of the Earth. Include a compass (as shown on page 17 of *Signs & Seasons*) and also familiar continents. Show the Earth's axis and include an arrow showing the direction of the Earth's rotation. Draw these twice more, showing changes as the Earth rotates.

Sun's Daily Motion

Draw an oval shape to show the horizon, wide enough to span the panel below. Include compass points. Draw the "dome of the firmament" above the horizon (as shown on page 36 of *Signs & Seasons*.) Show the proper position of the Sun in the sky at sunrise, mid-morning, noon, afternoon, and sunset. Sketch arrows showing the motion of the Sun. Add a person in the center of the compass, and show the shadows for each position of the Sun. Indicate the direction of the Sun's shadow over the course of the day. Confirm this motion with your backyard compass.

Historical Timeline

As you can see from the historical authors quoted throughout this book, Classical Astronomy has been understood and practiced throughout history. Use the table below to create a timeline of the names of these historical authors, showing the centuries in which they lived. Start with the Prologue and add to your timeline with each chapter.

600 B.C.	500 B.C.	400 B.C	300 B.C.	200 B.C.

100 B.C.	A.D	A.D 100	A.D 200	A.D 300

A.D 400	A.D 500	A.D 600	A.D 700	A.D 800

A.D 900	A.D 1000	A.D 1100	A.D 1200	A.D 1300

A.D 1400	A.D 1500	A.D 1600	A.D 1700	A.D 1800

Learn more about these authors and create journal entries about them on separate sheets. Include their locations, their positions of authority (if any), and their significance in western history and literature. Consult books and curricula from your family's library, as well as encyclopedias and the Internet. A biographical index of these authors is included in the Appendix of *Signs & Seasons*, and some of their major works are cited in the Bibliography.

Seeing the Horizon

Can you see the horizon from your house? If not, visit an open area, *e.g.* a field or other place with few nearby buildings or trees. Estimate the distance to the farthest objects (*i.e.* hundreds of feet or more than a mile.) Can you see the actual edge of the earth? Imagine the horizon as a big circle with you at the center. If you are near a hill or have access to a window in a tall building, notice that a more distant horizon can be seen. Record your notes below.

_____

_____

Globe Activities

Use a 12-inch rotating earth globe, preferably one from the George F. Cram Company that includes an *analemma*. Place the globe in a dark room with light shining in from the next room, preferably a small sized light. Show the proper rotation of the Earth. Note the sunrise terminator and the sunset terminator as the globe turns. Cut out or make a copy of the small "stickman" figure from the "volvelle" section and tape it to the globe over your own home location. Use your stickman to simulate sunrise, noon, and sunset as seen from your home.

When it is night over North America, where in the world is it daytime? When it is sunrise over your city, where is it sunset? Do this for several cities in the world and record your results.

_____

_____

For the Earth's rotation, if you're facing a globe so that north is "up," which direction would be the correct direction of rotation – right or left? Is there anything in television or movies that shows the rotation of the earth?

_____

_____

Here's an outside activity, to be done after dark with at least two people. Hold a flashlight or portable lantern several feet away from the globe to simulate the Sun.

To simulate the geocentric theory, have one person hold the light and walk around the globe in a circle toward the west to simulate daytime rotation. The other person locates your location on the globe with the stickman and notes the movement of the nighttime shadow behind the earth as the sun moves toward the west. Note the sunrise (where your home first enters the light) and the sunset (where your home first leaves the shadow).

_____

To simulate the heliocentric theory, one person holds the flashlight steady and the other person rotates the globe toward the east. Note the movement of your location as the Earth rotates toward the west. Note the sunrise (where your home first enters the light) and the sunset (where your home first enters the shadow).

_____

_____

For a sunrise, if north is up, which side of the Earth is in daylight (left or right)? (circle the correct answers) Which side is in night? (left or right) For sunset, if north is up, which side of the Earth is in daylight (left or right)? Which side is in night (left or right)?

_____

_____

Sun Volvelle

Make a volvelle to illustrate the daily motion of the Sun.
Necessary materials: volvelle components, string, brass fasteners (from an office supply store)

Cut out or make photocopies onto cardstock of the Sun Base Circle from page 93 and the Sun Wheel from pages 95 the Volvelle Section. Carefully punch holes in the centers of these two circles and insert a brass fastener.

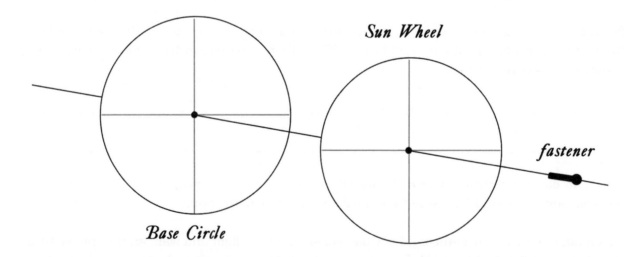

Each circle includes intersecting lines that cross in the centers of the circles. The Sun Wheel includes a small Sun about ¼ inch wide (or about ½ cm) at an end of one of the intersecting lines. The intersecting lines of the Sun Base Circle include a vertical line representing the *meridian* and a horizontal line representing the *horizon*. The Sun Base Circle includes a perimeter edge with *Noon* written at a top end of the meridian, and *Midnight* at a bottom end of the vertical line.

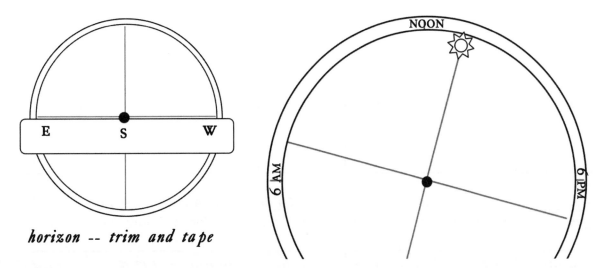

horizon -- trim and tape

The "eastern" end of the horizon line reads 6 am, and the "western" end of the horizon line reads 6 pm. The other times of day are indicated along the edge of the Sun Base Circle at the midpoints between the lines, with divisions to indicate the rest of the hours in a 24 hour day.

Cut out the Sun Volvelle Horizon from page 95 and match the edges of this piece to the edges of the Sun Base Circle. Be sure that the horizon piece is lined up to be parallel with the horizon line at 6 am and 6 pm on the Sun Base Circle, so that the intersecting line has *Noon* vertically at the top (as shown). The horizon piece will be lined up so that the left side reads *East* and the right side reads *West* as indicated. Tape the edges of the horizon piece in place onto the back side of the Sun Base Circle.

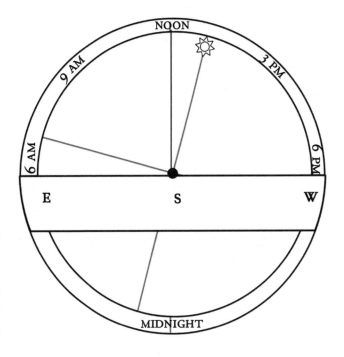

Tie a string around the brass fastener, loop it over the Noon mark, and tape the other end to the back of the Sun Base Circle to make a meridian.

You can now depict the Sun's passage for each hour of the day and night. Your volvelle can be "read" by using the Sun as an "hour hand." Set the position of the Sun to the desired time of day to see the approximate location of the Sun in the sky for that hour. Rotate the Sun Wheel to observe the passage of the Sun across the sky over a span of hours.

Practice using your Sun Volvelle to become familiar with its operation and to help illustrate how the Sun changes its position in the sky over a span of hours. You'll modify this volvelle in later chapters to include the phases of the Moon.

Using Your Volvelle

Record the number of hours the Sun takes to move through these fractions of its volvelle circle:

1/4 circle	1/2 circle	whole circle	1/3 circle	1/6 circle	1/12 circle	1/24 circle

We know from simple geometry that there are 360 degrees in a circle. Record the number of degrees that the Sun moves through the fractions of the circle for the hours listed above.

1/4 circle	1/2 circle	whole circle	1/3 circle	1/6 circle	1/12 circle	1/24 circle

How far does the Sun move across the sky in one hour? _____

Everyone has noticed that the days are longer in the summer and shorter in the winter. We'll learn more about this in later chapters of *Signs & Seasons*. Your simple Sun volvelle only indicates the average times of sunrise and sunset. However, the volvelle can still illustrate some simple things about the motion of the Sun.

When we go on daylight savings, the clocks are set ahead one hour, and we need to add an hour to the time indicated on the volvelle. In the table below, record the "clock times" during daylight savings when the Sun would reach the following positions on the volvelle:

6:00 A.M.	9:00 A.M.	Noon	6:00 P.M.	9:00 P.M.	Midnight

As the Sun circles the sky over the span of the day and through the night, it moves from east to west and back again. Use your volvelle to indicate whether the Sun is east or west of the meridian at the following times:

3:00 A.M.	6:00 A.M.	9:00 A.M.	3:00 P.M.	6:00 P.M.	9:00 P.M.

Field Activities for Chapter 2
The Darkness He Called Night

In this section, some activities require observing the sky late at night or early in the morning before sunrise. Have your parents accompany you or at least get their permission to be outside during these hours. It might be a good idea to schedule a family activity around a number of these observations, or do them while on a campout under dark skies away from the city lights.

N.B. – If you live on an "astronomically aligned" street, for backyard compass activities, try repeating the activities from your street, sidewalk and driveway.

Northern Constellations

Find the Big Dipper in the night sky. Use the "pointer" stars on the bowl of the Big Dipper to find Polaris. (This star is about as bright as the Dipper's stars, but can look faint as seen from the city). If the Big Dipper is not high overhead, find Cassiopeia on the other side of Polaris from the Big Dipper. Sketch these constellations as they appear in the sky. Record the date and time.

While standing in your backyard compass at night, face toward the north and then look up. Can you find Polaris from your compass? Note again the position of the Big Dipper. Is the Dipper to the east or to the west of Polaris? Indicate this on your sketch above.

Over a number of nights, practice finding the North Star from the Big Dipper. Look from different places other than home. In your journal, record the dates and times and the locations. Learn to use Polaris to find your direction at night. Make it a habit to find Polaris when you travel to different places after dark, including your regular places around your town (church, shopping, homes of friends and family, etc.) and if you travel long distances. For the 10 locations you observed in Chapter 1, visit them after dark. Find the North Star and use it to observe which side of the building faces north. Record your results and compare with the exposures you recorded in that activity.

Location	*North Side*	*Exposure*

Learn to find the constellation Orion

Since Orion is best seen when it's high in the sky above the south, find Orion during your current season. In the autumn, look in the early morning before sunrise. In early winter, Orion can best be found before midnight. In the early spring, look for Orion in the early evening, after sunset. Orion cannot be seen at all during the summer. (See the Appendix for a monthly list of the visibility of Orion.) Practice sketching Orion as you see it in the sky. Include every star you can see and notice if any are more or less visible on different nights.

First Night	*Second Night*	*Third Night*

Rotation around Polaris

Observe the rotation of the Dippers and Cassiopeia over two consecutive nights. For each night, sketch the positions of these constellations at the indicated times. Record the dates and times and indicate the number of hours elapsed between observations.

First Night - evening after nightfall	*First Night - midnight*	
Time and Date	*Time*	*Hrs. Elapsed*

Second Night - evening after nightfall	*Second Night — morning before sunrise*	
Time and Date	*Time*	*Hrs. Elapsed*

From your observations, estimate how many hours it would take for the northern constellations to complete one-quarter of a turn around Polaris. _____

How many hours for a half turn? _____ How many hours would it take to complete a full turn around Polaris? _____ If the Dipper is west of Polaris, how long will it take until Orion can be seen at the meridian? _____

Cardinal Line Activity

Just as you found a cardinal line from the Sun in the last chapter, you can also find a cardinal line from Polaris. Starting from the cardinal line of your backyard compass, take two sticks of uneven length and pound the longer one into the ground. Lying close to the ground, sight Polaris over the top of the stick. Take the shorter stick and hold it away from the longer stick. Find a place for the shorter stick where Polaris can be sighted over the tops of both of the sticks. Pound the shorter stick into the ground and confirm that Polaris can still be seen over the tops of both sticks. A line between the two sticks is a cardinal line that extends from north to south. Confirm that this cardinal line agrees with your compass's cardinal line. Record your observations.

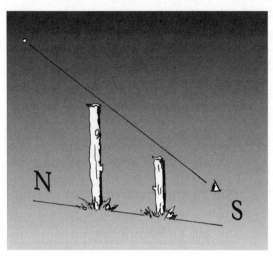 

Northern Stars Volvelle

Make a volvelle to illustrate the daily rotation of the northern stars.

As done with your Sun volvelle in Chapter 1, cut out or make copies on cardstock of the Northern Base Circle, Northern Sky Wheel and Northern Horizon piece from pages 97 and 99 in the volvelle

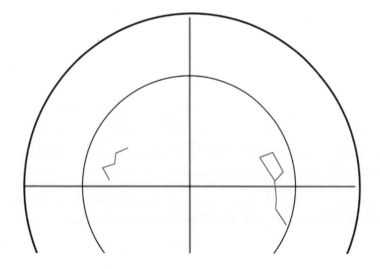 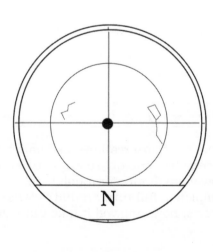

section. Carefully punch holes in the centers of the circles and join them together with a brass fastener. Tape the edges of the horizon piece to the Northern Base Circle in the indicated places. Loop some string around the brass fastener and over the top to simulate the meridian.

Rotate the Northern Wheel counterclockwise to simulate the rotation of the northern constellations. Later chapters will explain how to find the orientation of the northern constellations for any time of day, every month of the year! You'll use your volvelle in the next activity.

Meridian Activities

While standing in your backyard compass, look straight up overhead to the zenith. Turn to look over at the North Star and then down to the northern horizon. Follow the line back to the zenith and down to the southern horizon. Imagine the meridian as a circle spanning the sky through these points. Repeat this experiment facing in each direction of your backyard compass, turning your head from north to south. Record your notes and any other interesting observations.

_____

_____

_____

On any given night, locate the Big Dipper and Cassiopeia with respect to the North Star. Are either at the meridian? Are they east or west of the meridian? Record your observation results with date and time. Using your volvelle and the results of the observations above, estimate the number of hours before either the Dipper or Cassiopeia reaches the meridian on that night. If one of these constellations will be visible at the meridian before sunrise, confirm your estimate by going outside to observe. Record several different dates and times.

Date and Time	Position of Dipper	Time til Meridian	Position of Cassiopeia	Time til Meridian

Observe the stars near the meridian. Observe bright stars in the skies to the east and west of the meridian. Come back in an hour – are the stars that were near the meridian more toward the east or west? Are they higher or lower in the sky? Are the stars in the eastern sky higher? Are the stars in the western sky lower? Have any moved along the meridian? Check in another hour and compare the results. On the next page, sketch any prominent stars and record the dates and times of each observation.

Repeat these observations over a several day period, checking the sky at different times of the night. On Day 1 – check the sky in the early evening; Day 2 – before midnight, Day 3 – at midnight. Sketch your observations and try to notice if you can observe any of the same stars. You might be able to use this information in later chapters. Record the dates and times of your observations.

Day 1 – Early Evening	Day 1 - Second Observation	
Time and Date	Time	Hrs. Elapsed

Day 2 – Before Midnight	Day 2 - Second Observation	
Time and Date	Time	Hrs. Elapsed

Day 3 – Around Midnight	Day 3 - Second Observation	
Time and Date	Time	Hrs. Elapsed

Globe Activity

Use the globe to demonstrate the rotation of the northern constellations.

Sketch the Big Dipper and Cassiopeia onto a cardboard pizza box. Place a dowel rod or a bar or pipe through the location of Polaris. Line up the dowel rod with the axis of your 12 inch globe, with your "stickman" taped to the globe along the Equator. Turn the dowel rod to rotate the constellations counterclockwise, sighting them from along the edge of the globe, from behind the stickman. Then hold the dowel rod still and turn the globe toward the east, still sighting from behind the cut-out. Compare how the rotation of the globe causes a shift in the apparent positions of the constellations.

Circumpolar Circle Activity

While observing the Big Dipper or Cassiopeia near the meridian in the previous section, determine whether each constellation is within your local circumpolar circle. Is either constellation above the horizon when at lower meridian, below the North Star?

_____

_____

_____

Note – the circumpolar circles change with latitude. The Dippers and Cassiopeia can be seen at all times from latitude 40 degrees north and points north. 40°N is near the cities of New York, Boston, Philadelphia, Cleveland, Chicago, Denver, and San Francisco. New England, the northern Plains States, the Pacific Northwest, Canada, Britain, and Alaska are all farther north.

However, in the Southern USA, especially points south of 30°N such as Florida, South Texas, and Southern California, the circumpolar circles are smaller, and the Big Dipper and Cassiopeia actually set when at the lower meridian!

Direction Activity

Use a pizza box or another piece of cardboard to make a "reversed" compass to represent the sky, as shown in the chapter, with east to the left and west to the right. Stand in your backyard compass while holding the reversed compass while facing the south. Note that both compasses point towards same horizons – north, east, west and south.

Hold your reversed compass overhead, at zenith. Note that it still points "north" i.e. toward the North Star. Lean further backward, holding your reversed compass along the meridian until it approaches the North Star. Note that "north" is the direction along the meridian *toward* Polaris, and "south" is the direction along the meridian *away from* the Polaris. Become familiar with the concept of the sky being divided by the meridian into two halves – an eastern "rising" half and a western "setting" half.

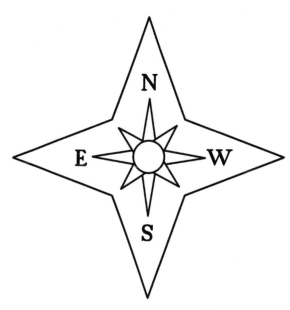

Celestial Globe Activity

Obtain a styrofoam ball from a craft store, preferably 5 or 6 inches (15 cm) or larger. Draw 2 dots on opposite sides to represent the poles. Draw a circle between the poles at an equal distance from each. If the ball already has "poles" and an "equator" from the molding process, use these, and draw over those features with a marker. This shows that the celestial equator in the sky is similar to the terrestrial equator on the earth – a circle that is exactly centered between the two poles.

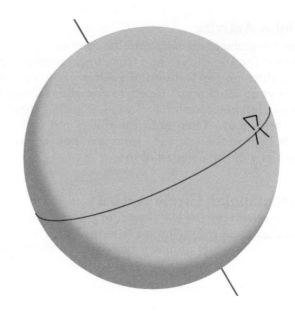

Add to the equator a small pattern of the constellation Orion. You'll add more features to this celestial globe in later chapters.

Celestial Equator Activities

If possible, find Orion at meridian. Look at the right hour for the season (fall mornings, winter midnight, evenings of early spring. See the Appendix of *Signs & Seasons* for a monthly list.) Observe Orion from your backyard compass. Do one of the following in the left space below:

1) If Orion is near the meridian. note the height in the sky of Orion's belt as compared to objects on the ground – trees, buildings, telephone pole, etc. Sketch this scene in one of the panels below. Practice using this to determine the location in the sky of the celestial equator when Orion is not visible.

2) If Orion is after rising or before setting, confirm that it rises due east and sets due west. Sketch Orion rising or setting with the time and date of the observation.

If Orion is high in the sky, look due east in your backyard compass. Turn your eyes from the eastern horizon, up through Orion's belt, and follow toward the due west point on the horizon. Turn and look at Polaris. Imagine the celestial equator as a circle that is exactly in the middle of the starry sky between the poles. In the right space below, draw a half-circle representing the celestial sphere and an ellipse to represent the horizon. Draw dots for the celestial poles and an oblique circle that represents the celestial equator, passing through Orion's belt, as shown in *Signs & Seasons*.

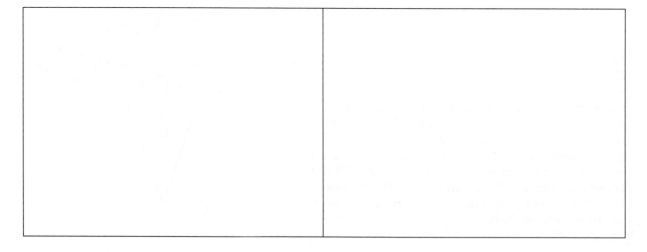

Orion Volvelle

Make a volvelle to illustrate Orion on the Celestial Equator

Cut out or make a copy on cardstock of the Orion Base Circle from page 101 and the Orion Wheel and Orion Volvelle Horizon from pages 103 and 105. Carefully punch holes in the centers of the circles and insert a brass fastener. Attach the Orion Volvelle Horizon along the bottom and tape it to the back of the Base Circle. Loop some string around the brass fastener and over the top to simulate the meridian.

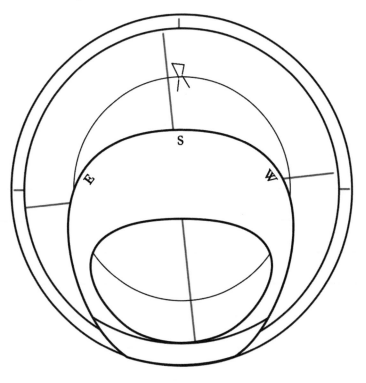

You can now depict Orion's passage over the span of the night. You can read this volvelle by pointing the vertical line near Orion to a time and count the hours that elapse as this constellation moves across the sky.

The hours on this volvelle do not yet signify any actual times associated with Orion's appearance in the sky. In later chapters, you modify your volvelle that includes constellations and other information to assist you in understanding the passage of the seasons. It will also include a Sun to enable you to use the hours on the Base Circle to make actual readings. At this point, you can use the hours on the Base Circle to measure the time required for Orion to cross the sky.

Rotate the Orion Wheel clockwise to simulate the daily rotation of Orion along the celestial equator. Practice using your Sun Volvelle to become familiar with its operation and to help illustrate how Orion changes its position in the sky over a span of hours.

Using Your Volvelle

Note the locations on the horizon piece where Orion rises and sets. How many hours does Orion take to reach the meridian after rising? How long is Orion above the horizon each day? After setting, how long does Orion take to reach the lower meridian? How long does Orion spend below the horizon?

Place where Orion Rises	Place where Orion Sets	Time til Meridian	Time Above Horizon	Time til Lower Merid.	Time Below Horizon

Additional Notes

_____

_____

_____

_____

_____

_____

_____

_____

_____

_____

_____

_____

_____

_____

_____

_____

_____

_____

_____

_____

_____

_____

_____

_____

_____

_____

_____

Basic Definitions

Using your family dictionary, look up the words "waxing" and "waning." Write these definitions below in your own words. Include explanations of the best times of day for sighting the Moon when it is in these phases.

Waxing _____

_____

_____

Waning _____

_____

_____

Moon Phases – First Month

Use a wall calendar, newspaper or other reference to find out the date of the next New Moon. Over the next couple nights after the New Moon, look for a thin crescent Moon in the western sky during evening twilight after sunset. In the panel below, record the date, time and appearance of the first sighting of the waxing crescent Moon.

Sketch the appearance of the Moon, noting its thickness and distance above the horizon and from the place of the sunset. Note the direction on the compass and include ground objects such as trees, buildings and telephone poles for reference points. (See the top figure on page 65 of *Signs & Seasons*.) To get a nice, uniform circle, draw your Moons with a template. (Make your circles small, about ¼ inch (0.5 cm)). Draw the curve of the Moon's terminator, and color in the dark side of the Moon. Clear skies permitting, look at the same time the next day. Observe how far the Moon has traveled across the sky in only a single day. Label your Moons with the dates and times. Repeat each night until First Quarter.

Waxing Crescent Moon

During thin crescent phases – observe the Earthshine
In the early waxing crescent phases, notice and record changes in Earthshine each evening as it waxes from a thin crescent to a half moon. Sketch what you see, including date and time. Draw these pictures larger, and maybe use a large coin as a template.

Observe Moon Shadows – also note the evening when you can first see shadows cast by the Moon's light. This will depend on the clarity of the atmosphere and the amount of ground lighting in your area. Also, notice that the fainter stars become harder to see as the thin crescent Moon waxes and grows brighter.

_____

_____

_____

Draw a "celestial" picture of the Moon in orbit around the Earth (similar to the top left figure on page 58 of *Signs & Seasons*). Correlate the Moon's orbital positions with the waxing crescent phases depicted in the previous drawing.

Waxing Crescent Moon – Celestial View

Waxing Gibbous Phases – First Quarter through Full Moon
Repeat the above sketching activity to show the First Quarter and waxing gibbous phases, through the Full Moon. Be sure to indicate relative direction as seen from your backyard compass and show trees or other ground objects.

Waxing Gibbous Moon

At the First Quarter, note the position of the Moon around sunset, one hour afterwards, and another hour after that. Sketch the Moon according to your observations and indicate the times next to your Moon sketches.

First Quarter Moon – Movement Across the Sky

Observe the Man in the Moon
During the thick gibbous and full phases, sketch the Moon with the "maria" (dark features). Can you spot the "man in the moon"? These features are easiest to see in bright twilight, or if a gibbous Moon or Full Moon is rising orange, low in the evening sky. It has hard to see these features at night since the Moon is so bright. Notice how the face on the Moon is revealed as the phases increase and decrease. Using other resources (encyclopedias or the Internet) learn the names of the "seas" on the Moon, and correlate them with the features of the Moon's face.

Draw a "celestial" view of the Moon's orbit corresponding to the waxing gibbous phases, from First Quarter through the Full Moon, as you did for the waxing crescent phases.

Waxing Gibbous Moon — Celestial View

After the Full Moon, note the risings of the waning gibbous Moon. As with the previous sketches, record the time after dark when you first see the Moon and sketch the appearance of its waning phase as it rises, including its direction as seen from your backyard compass. Repeat the above for five days afterwards, or until the Moon is rising too late to be seen before bedtime.

Waning Gibbous Moon — Risings

Waning Gibbous Phases – After Full Moon through Last Quarter

Starting in the waning gibbous phases, get up early before sunrise and look for the Moon in the morning sky. As you did for the waxing phases above, observe at the same time and sketch the appearances of the waning Moon over a period of days, including direction. Note how far across the sky the Moon has traveled since the evening before.

Waning Gibbous Moon

Draw a "celestial" view of the Moon's orbit corresponding to the waning gibbous phases, from Full Moon through Last Quarter, as you did for the waxing phases.

Waning Gibbous Moon — Celestial View

Observe the waning crescent phases before sunrise in the mornings after Last Quarter. As above, sketch the appearances of the waning Moon over a period of days, including direction, showing the thickness of the crescent and the position in the sky.

Waning Crescent Moon

Draw a "celestial" view of the Moon's orbit corresponding to the waning crescent phases, from Last Quarter through Full Moon.

Waning Crescent Moon — Celestial View

Moon Phases – Second Month

Observe and record the risings and settings of the Moon, and note how these change with each phase. Find the Moon's rising and setting times. Consult the weather section of the newspaper or the U.S. Naval Observatory web site, listed in the Introduction. Record this information each day for a complete lunar month in the table (below), starting with the New Moon. Subtract each day's rising and setting times from the days before or after to measure the exact difference from day to day. How close are these differences to 48 minutes?

Date	Moonrise	Difference	Moonset	Difference	Phase

NOTE! Things to Keep in Mind

The Moon will often "rise" at a certain date and "set" at a time after Midnight the next day. Be sure to keep your rising and setting times together for each "lunar day" – one complete interval of the Moon above and below the horizon. The papers publish only the rising and setting times of the Moon that occur on that particular date. This can be misleading since the "moonset" of the previous "lunar day" can be shown at an earlier time than the "moonrise" of the next "lunar day." Be sure to compare your rising and setting data from the days in the newspaper or on the web.

Also, there will be days in each lunar month when the Moon does not "rise" and "set." Because the Moon rises about 48 minutes later each day, the Moon's daily cycle between risings is longer than 24 hours. There are times when it rises or sets shortly *before Midnight* on one day, and does not rise or set again until *after Midnight* the next day!

Weather permitting, try to observe the Moon rising or setting at these times. If you don't have a clear horizon, look an hour or so after moonrise or before moonset. Be sure to look during the daytime, since the Moon is usually easy to see in the bright daytime sky. Sketch any interesting observations in the space below.

Using a wall calendar, note the dates of the Moon's quarters. Count the number of days between quarters and confirm the length of the lunar month.

Quarter	Date	Date of Previous Quarter	Difference
New Moon			
First Quarter			
Full Moon			
Last Quarter			
New Moon			
		Total	

At the Movies
Next Easter, if you see the movie *The Ten Commandments*, note that the "plague of the firstborn" is incorrectly shown occurring during a waning crescent, not a Full Moon as it should be on the night of Passover. However, *The Passion of the Christ* accurately shows Jesus in the Garden of Gethsemane under a Full Moon.

Moon Phases – Third Month
Moonfinding - observe the Moon each day as it crosses the meridian.

Create a chart of the times of moonrise and moonset, beginning on the New Moon. Indicate the principal phases (e.g. waxing crescent, waxing gibbous, etc.) and quarters. Count the number of hours between moonrise and 12:00 P.M. and then 12:00 P.M. and moonset to find the Moon's time in the sky above the horizon. Divide that number of hours by two and add that to the moonrise time. This will be approximately the time when the moon transits the meridian. (**N.B.** – be careful – for a date when the moonset is before the moonrise, count that moonset with the previous day's moonrise.) Observe the Moon at these times from your backyard compass.

Date	Phase	Moonrise	Moonset	Hrs. in the Sky	Transit Time

For the table below, write the times for sunrise and sunset. Count the number of hours between sunrise and 12:00 P.M. and then 12:00 P.M. and sunset to find the total hours of daylight. Add that to the sunrise time. This will be the clock time for "High Noon." Write down the Moon Transit times from the previous table and record the difference in the time between High Noon and the time of the Moon's transit, indicating the lag of the Moon behind the Sun.

Date	Sunrise	Sunset	Hrs. Daylight	High Noon	Moon Transit	Difference

For the tables created above, stand in your backyard compass and look for the Moon at the meridian each day at the calculated times. Spend some time looking if the Moon is not easily visible. In the crescent phases, when the Moon crosses the meridian during the day, try standing in shadows of a building to block the glare of the Sun. *Never look directly at the Sun!!!*

Globe Activity

Demonstrate the Moon's orbital motion and its phases.

Using your 12-inch globe, take a softball to represent the Moon. In your backyard, place the softball 30 feet away from the globe (9 meters). This accurately shows the proportional distance between the Earth and the Moon. In your backyard, pound a stick near the "Earth," and loop 30 feet of rope around the stake. If working on pavement, use chalk to trace a circle having a 30 foot radius.

Place a basketball or beach ball somewhere very far away to represent the position of the sun. Following the end of the rope, walk the "Moon" around the "Earth" to different positions, counterclockwise around the globe, to represent its orbital motion. Leaning over the "Earth," sight along its edge as it rotates to observe the rising and setting of the Sun with respect to the Moon's position.

At nighttime, allow a distant light (e.g. a flashlight or portable gas lamp, etc.) to shine on the globe and softball. Observe the terminators on the globe and softball. Looking from the globe, as the "Moon" moves around its orbital circle, notice the changes in the terminator. Note the position of the Moon in its orbit when the quarters, crescent phases, and gibbous phases are observed. Record any interesting observations.

_____

_____

_____

_____

_____

Volvelle Activity

Modify your Sun volvelle from Chapter 1 to include Moon Phases.

Dismantle your Sun volvelle. Cut out or copy the Moon Phase Wheel from page 107 of the Volvelle Section and use that instead of the Sun Wheel from Chapter 1.

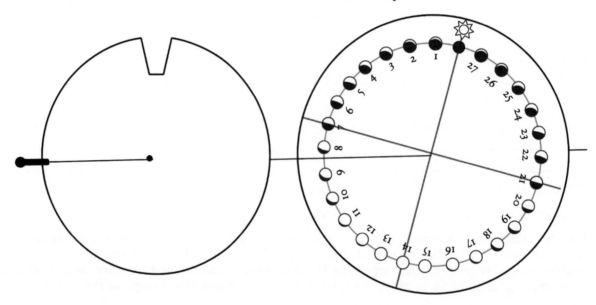

Cut out or copy the Window Wheel from page 109 of the Volvelle Section. Poke a hole in the center and assemble the wheels with the Window Wheel on top. The Window Wheel reveals a selected Moon phase (and age) for a selected day and hides all the others.

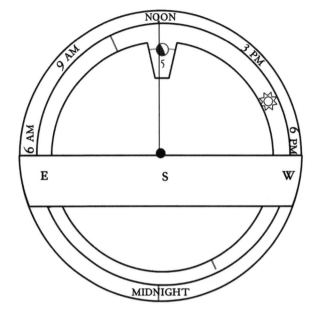

Using the Sun-Moon Volvelle
*   Line up the Sun with a desired hour to depict the sky at that time of day.

*   Line up the notch in the window wheel to reveal a selected "age" of the Moon, i.e. the number of days since the New Moon, and the phase of the Moon that corresponds to that age.

*   Turn the wheels together to show how the Moon rises, transits and sets as compared with the Sun. As you rotate the Sun and Moon phase wheel to change the time of day, make sure that you move the window wheel also so that the same age of the Moon is displayed, so as to simulate the daily motion of both the Sun and the Moon for that particular phase of the Moon.

Using Your Volvelle
*   Turn the window wheel to the New Moon. Set the movable wheels so that the Sun and New Moon are at 6:00 AM. Turn the wheels together to show how the New Moon rises, transits and sets with the Sun.

*   Turn the window wheel to reveal the first waxing crescent phase. Turn the wheels together to show how the waxing crescent rises, transits and sets *after* the Sun. Repeat for all the waxing crescent phases, observing how the Moon follows the Sun by a greater amount each day.

*   Tell time by the Sun on the volvelle. Dial in a First Quarter Moon, and notice that when the Sun is at 6:00 PM, the Moon is at the meridian. For each phase, you can approximately determine the Moon's transit times by aligning the Moon with the meridian and reading the time on the outer wheel that is aligned with the Sun. Compare with the calculated times from the previous section.

*   Repeat the above activity for the Full Moon and Last Quarter. Note the times when the Moon rises, transits, and sets. As above, compare these times with the calculated times from the previous section.

*   Using your volvelle, make a table comparing times of moonrise, transit, and moonset. For each age of the Moon, record the times of moonrise, transit, and moonset as compared with the Sun. Express these times as being after the Sun, e.g. moonrise being "X" number of hours after the sunrise, etc. (Try to estimate fractions of an hour, e.g. 45 minutes as being 3/4 hour, etc.) Record your results in the table below. How do these times compare with the data compiled in the tables for Month 3?

N.B.: *This volvelle only shows approximate times since sunrise and sunset times vary considerably over the span of a year.*

Age of Moon	Moonrise (Time After Sunrise)	Moon Transit (Time After Noon)	Moonset (Time After Sunset)

Please Note:

In this section, you will begin to learn the constellations. There is an Appendix of constellation tables in Signs & Seasons *that will help you learn the best times to find the constellations and the bright stars. However, there is one point that needs to be emphasized -- **learning the constellations requires WORK**. You won't learn anything if you poke your head out for one minute and then give up. And you can't learn all the constellations in just one night.*

As you work at learning the constellations, you will make mistakes and get confused. You might learn some one night and be unable to find them the next night. You might forget everything you learn and need to start over. It might be quite frustrating. This is all a normal part of the process. Also, the bright planets can add to the confusion, since they are brighter than the stars, and can mess up the appearance of the constellations until you learn the patterns.

*Learning the sky requires **persistent** and **regular** effort. You might need to spend at least 15 minutes to a half-hour on clear nights, over a period of weeks and months. It will probably take you at least a whole year to learn the entire sky, a complete annual cycle of constellations.*

However, if you do learn the sky, the benefits are great. Once you learn the stars, you will know them for the rest of your life. You can learn to tell time and navigate by the stars. You can see the same stars from anywhere in the world. They will make your travel experiences more rich and interesting, and be a familiar sight while abroad. And as everything in your life changes over the years, the stars won't. They will be the same as they've always been through all history.

Visibility of the Night Sky

Most of the star scenes in *Signs & Seasons* depict a fully dark night sky, as God created it, as can be seen from rural areas. However, your ability to see all these stars depends on the weather and also if you live in a city with a lot of street lighting.

Some constellations won't be visible at all from brightly-lit urban areas. However, it might actually be easier to pick out some constellations from a city sky with fewer stars. On a clear night under an unspoiled rural sky, many stars are visible, and it can be hard to pick out constellations because so many stars appear so bright.

Wherever you are, not many stars can be seen under moonlight, since the glare of this natural "light pollution" hides the dimmer stars. When the Moon is waxing, you can best find the constellations after the Moon has set. During the waning Moon, the skies are darkest in the evening, before the Moon rises.

Even from a dark sky location, not many stars can be seen if the weather is hazy, and obviously none can be seen if it's cloudy. The clearest night skies are on days with low humidity, when the Sun's shadows are very dark. Grey, fuzzy Sun shadows always mean hazy skies.

Note: if you have difficulty finding the zodiac constellations, feel free to combine these activities with the constellation observing activities in Chapter 6.

Sketching Activities
Sketch the Zodiac Constellations

Referring to the constellation tables in the Appendix of *Signs & Seasons*, find the zodiac constellations visible near the meridian for the early evening hours for your current month. Also find the constellations visible at midnight and in the morning before sunrise. Sketch the "connect-the-dot" patterns shown in Chapter 4 for these zodiac constellations. It would be much easier to find the constellations if you could see those connecting lines! But the constellation patterns are generally formed from the brightest stars visible in each part of the sky. Once you learn to recognize those patterns, it's easier to visualize the connections between the stars that form the patterns.

Evening	*Midnight*	*Morning*

In the spaces below, sketch six more zodiac constellations of your choosing. Indicate times and dates when these constellations can be seen near the meridian.

Constellation — Time and Date	*Constellation — Time and Date*	*Constellation — Time and Date*

Constellation — Time and Date	*Constellation — Time and Date*	*Constellation — Time and Date*

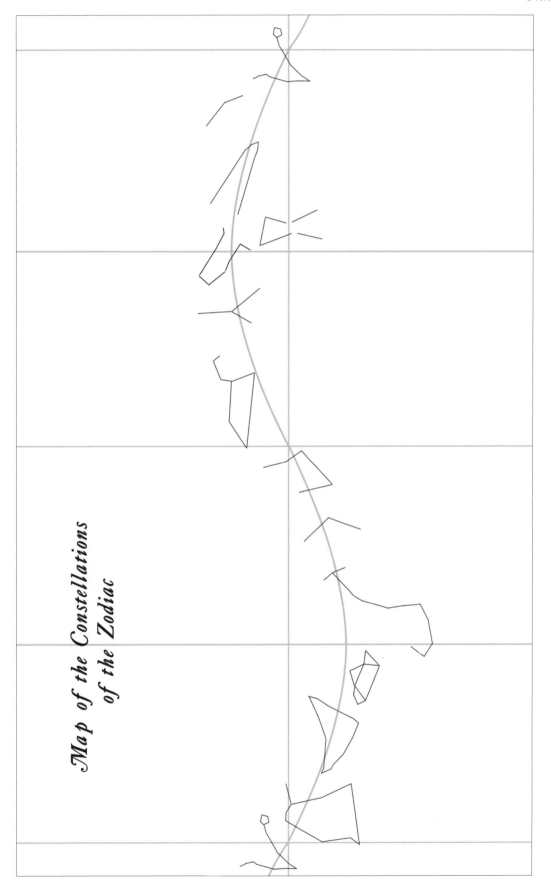

Map of the Constellations
of the Zodiac

Flat Map of the Zodiac
Refer to the "zodiac map" on the previous page. Label the constellations indicated, including Orion and the zodiac constellations. Indicate the celestial equator and also the places of the equinoxes and solstices. You will use this map in later activity sections.

Observing the Constellations

Observing Orion
Referring to Table I in the Appendix, find the best time for viewing Orion in your current month (in all seasons except summer). Upon finding Orion, find Gemini and Taurus, as shown in Chapter 4. Sketch the constellations as they appear in the sky. Record the date and time.

Observing the Zodiac
Evening – Referring again to the constellation tables in the Appendix, find the zodiac constellation visible near the meridian in the evening for your date. If you can't find it, look for a different one in a couple hours before bedtime. Record your results. How does the actual appearance of the constellation compare with your previous sketches? Can you see all the stars, or are the faint ones invisible? Have you spotted a planet? (Consult the planet tables in the Appendix for the current location of the planets.) Use your reverse compass to find your direction in the sky. Can you identify any zodiac constellations to the east or west of the meridian?

_____

_____

_____

Midnight – Repeat the above for the zodiac constellation at the meridian at midnight. How does this compare to your observations of the sky in the early evening? Can you identify any other zodiac constellations rising or setting?

_____

_____

_____

Morning – Observe the zodiac constellations at the meridian in the morning before sunrise. How does this compare to your observations at midnight? How has the sky changed over the night? Can you tell which zodiac constellations are higher or lower in the sky?

_____

_____

_____

For Observers in the City

Observe zodiac constellations from home as noted above, recording the date and time of your observations. Sketch the constellations as they appear under the city lights, including all the visible stars. Compare with the star patterns shown in the book. Indicate if any stars cannot be found from your home. Also, add comments as to the brightness of the visible the stars.

Follow-up and observe the sky from a dark-sky location, perhaps during a camp out or other trip to a rural location. Repeat the sketch activity and indicate if more stars are visible. Add comments as to whether the stars appear brighter than in the city.

Identifying Stars
Of the constellations you learned in Chapter 4, can you determine if any of the bright stars were observed in the meridian activity of Chapter 2? If so, record the star names and constellations.

_____

_____

_____

Observing the Celestial Equator
Looking from your backyard compass or your "equator spot" from Chapter 2, observe Virgo in the sky near the meridian. Note that these stars are nearly as high above the horizon as Orion. Also, observe the "water jar" in Aquarius and the "circlet" in Pisces. Can you tell that these stars are about as high in the sky as Orion's belt?

_____

_____

_____

Observing the Northern Sky
While observing the zodiac constellations, turn around and observe the positions of the Dippers and Cassiopeia. When Gemini is at the meridian, the Big Dipper is east of Polaris. When Leo is at the meridian, the Big Dipper is overhead, close to Leo (more in Chapter 6). When Scorpius and Sagittarius are near the meridian, the Big Dipper is west of Polaris. When Pisces and Aries are near the meridian, Cassiopeia is overhead.

In the table below, record the zodiac constellations near the meridian at any time of night on any given day. Record the position of the Big Dipper and Cassiopeia at these times, e.g. to the left or right of Polaris, at the meridian, or in the trees. Alternatively, judge the positions of the northern constellations corresponding to a position on the clock face, e.g. "the two o'clock position," etc. Repeat this activity at different dates and times over a period of months.

Date	Time	Constellation at Meridian	Big Dipper	Cassiopeia

Observe Risings and Settings of the Zodiac
Once you become familiar with the constellations of the zodiac, try to observe them at their risings and settings. Northern constellations rise and set toward the north, and southern constellations rise and set to the south.

Modify your backyard compass. Add four more marker stones between the cardinal stones to indicate NE, NW, SE and SW.

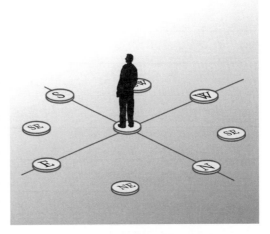

Find the positions of rising and setting constellations with respect to your backyard compass. Whichever constellation you can find at the meridian, look one-quarter of the way around the zodiac on either side to find the stars that are rising and setting. For example, if Gemini is at meridian, Pisces is setting due west and Virgo is rising due east. Also, if Virgo is at the meridian, Gemini is setting in the northwest and Sagittarius is rising in the southeast. Sketch the constellations you see and record the dates and times.

Constellation Rising	*Constellation at Meridian*	*Constellation Setting*
General Direction	*Date and Time*	*General Direction*

Constellation Rising	*Constellation at Meridian*	*Constellation Setting*
General Direction	*Date and Time*	*General Direction*

Research Activity

Learn about precession. Read up in the encyclopedias and on the Internet and record your results below.

_____

_____

_____

_____

_____

_____

_____

_____

Celestial Globe Activity

Using the Celestial Globe you created in Chapter 2, make a mark on the equator opposite Orion, and two small marks at equal distances in between on the equator. Measure the distance between one of the Poles to Orion, and find the midpoint. Find the distance between that midpoint and Orion, and place a dot at that point. Find the opposite mark on the equator from Orion, and at an equal distance below the equator, make another dot. Connect these dots above and below the equator to make a slanted circle around the globe, passing through the other marks on the equator in between. This slanted circle will represent the ecliptic.

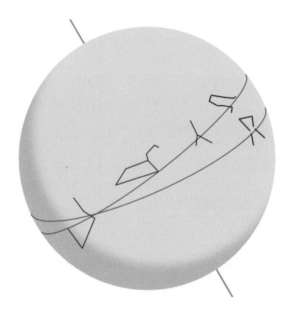

The extreme points of the slanted circle will represent the solstices, while the crossing points at the equator will represent the equinoxes. At the extreme points above Orion, draw a small figure of the star pattern for Gemini. At the opposite extreme point, draw the pattern for Sagittarius. At the intersecting point to the right of Gemini and Orion, draw the pattern for Pisces. And at the other intersecting point, draw Virgo. Fill in the other zodiac constellations in between.

Your celestial globe is an *inverted globe*. The actual sky appears to be *concave*, with the constellations on the *inside* of the sphere. But with this plan, we can place the constellations on the *convex exterior* of the sphere – an opposite arrangement to the real sky. We'll add more to our sphere in later chapters.

Volvelle Activity
Modified Orion Volvelle from Chapter 2 including Zodiac Constellations
Use the Orion volvelle you made in Chapter 2. You can either dismantle it or create a new volvelle for this activity by making new copies of the Base Circle and the Orion Horizon piece. Find the Zodiac Wheel on page 111 in the Volvelle Section.

Cut out the Zodiac Wheel or make a cardstock copy and use this wheel instead of the Orion Wheel of the volvelle. Assemble the components of your modified volvelle as you did in previous sections.

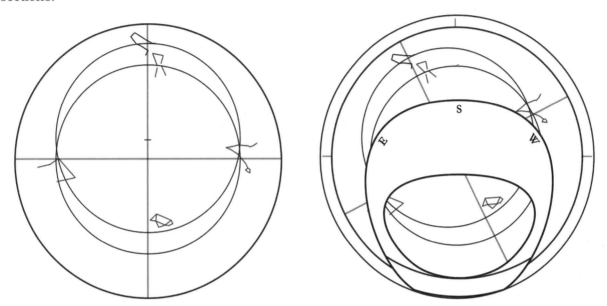

Note that the Zodiac Wheel includes the zodiac constellations and the ecliptic circle, in addition to Orion and the celestial equator. The perpendicular lines on the Zodiac Wheel represent the lines of the solstices and equinoxes.

On the ecliptic circle above Orion, Gemini is shown at the point of the summer solstice. On the opposite side, Sagittarius is shown at the position of the winter solstice. Pisces and Virgo are shown at the respective intersecting points of the ecliptic and celestial equator corresponding to the equinoxes. The other constellations of the ecliptic are at their respective points, as shown in *Signs & Seasons*.

Using your volvelle
*   Label the constellations on the Zodiac Wheel. Use abbreviations and write small so as to not take up too much space and clutter up your volvelle.

*   Rotate the Zodiac Wheel and observe the places where the ecliptic crosses the horizon. Note how the ecliptic circle moves from north to south along the eastern and western horizons with each turn of the wheel. Also notice how the celestial equator does not change as the wheel turns, but always crosses the horizon at due east and due west.

*   Observe the meridian as the wheel turns. Notice how the ecliptic circle is successively higher and lower above the celestial equator with each turn of the wheel.

In the next chapter you will modify your volvelle to include a Constellation Wheel with months and a transparent Sun Wheel to illustrate the Sun's annual motion along the ecliptic.

Using your volvelle, record the directions on the horizon where the following constellations can be found while rising and setting. Also record where these constellations can be found at the meridian with respect to the celestial equator.

Direction	Pisces	Gemini	Virgo	Sagittarius
Rising				
Setting				
Meridian				

For each of the constellations in the table below, use the hours along the Base Circle to estimate the amount of time between rising and setting. Record the constellation at the opposite horizon from each constellation, i.e. the one that is rising while the other sets, or visa versa. Estimate the amount of time between rising and setting for each opposite constellation. Add these two times together. Do you notice a pattern?

Constellation	Time - Rising and Setting	Opposite Constellation	Time - Rising and Setting	Total - Two Times
Pisces				
Aries				
Taurus				
Gemini				
Cancer				
Leo				
Virgo				
Libra				
Scorpius				
Sagittarius				
Capricornus				
Aquarius				

Field Activities for Chapter 5
The Cycle of the Year

N.B.: *Many of these activities include making observations and recording data in tables over the same span of months. Therefore, review these activities before starting this chapter and work on them concurrently.*

Research Activities

Make a table of rising and setting times for the Sun for your hometown at about weekly intervals for the span of one year. You can collect this information in advance from The Old Farmer's Almanac, or from the U.S. Naval Observatory web site, mentioned in the Instructions.

Date	Sunrise	Sunset		Date	Sunrise	Sunset

Hours of Daylight

Make a chart of sunrise and sunset times at your location for one day a week for six months from the summer solstice to the winter solstice. Include a column for the number of hours of daylight. Find this by counting the hours between sunrise and 12:00 P.M., and from between 12:00 P.M. and sunset. Include a column for the time of "High Noon," when the Sun reaches the meridian. Find this by dividing the number of hours in the day by two, and add that number of hours to the time of sunrise.

Date	Sunrise	Sunset	Hrs. Daylight	High Noon

From your chart on the previous page, notice the times of sunrise and sunset. In what months do these times change quickly from day to day? In what months do these times change slowly? Notice how there is little variation a month before and after the solstices, and how quickly the sunset times change for a month before and after the equinoxes. Make a double graph plotting these sunrise and sunset times for each week of the month from the summer solstice to the winter solstice.

Time	June				July				August				September				October				November				December			
	1	*2*	*3*	*4*	*1*	*2*	*3*	*4*	*1*	*2*	*3*	*4*	*1*	*2*	*3*	*4*	*1*	*2*	*3*	*4*	*1*	*2*	*3*	*4*	*1*	*2*	*3*	*4*
11:00 P.M																												
10:00 P.M												Time of Sunset																
9:00 P.M																												
8:00 P.M																												
7:00 P.M																												
6:00 P.M																												
5:00 P.M																												
4:00 P.M																												
3:00 P.M																												
2:00 P.M																												
1:00 P.M																												
12:00 P.M																												
11:00 A.M																												
10:00 A.M																												
9:00 A.M																												
8:00 A.M																												
7:00 A.M																												
6:00 A.M																												
5:00 A.M																												
4:00 A.M																												
3:00 A.M																												
2:00 A.M																												
1:00 A.M												Time of Sunrise																
12:00 A.M																												
Time	*1*	*2*	*3*	*4*	*1*	*2*	*3*	*4*	*1*	*2*	*3*	*4*	*1*	*2*	*3*	*4*	*1*	*2*	*3*	*4*	*1*	*2*	*3*	*4*	*1*	*2*	*3*	*4*
	June				July				August				September				October				November				December			

Flat Map Activity

Use the flat map on the next page as you did in Chapter 4. Draw small pictures of the Sun on the map as follows, or else get some small Sun stickers from a craft shop (these are usually easily available). Place a Sun on your map at the point of the vernal equinox in Pisces, and label it March 21. Place another sticker at the summer solstice in Gemini, and label it June 21. Repeat for the autumnal equinox and the winter solstice. After the four seasonal points are in place, add Suns to each of the other zodiac constellations, and label each the 21st of the respective month. (For example, label the Sun near Aries April 21 and the Sun by Taurus May 21.) This roughly shows the apparent position of the Sun on the ecliptic during each month of the year.

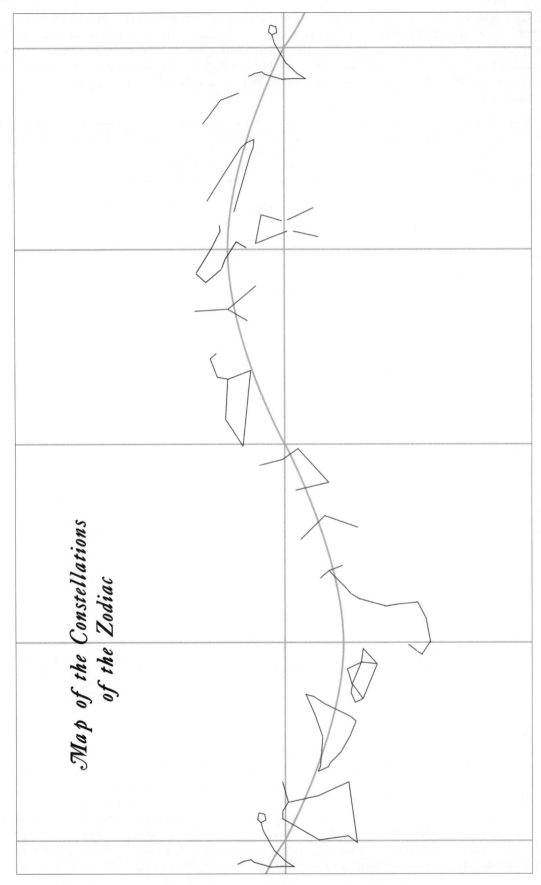

Map of the Constellations
of the Zodiac

Solar System Map

Use the following overhead view maps of the solar system to show how the changing orbital position of the Earth results in the changes in the apparent position of the Sun against the background constellations of the zodiac. Behind each constellation outline, write the name of a month as follows: *Pisces – March, Gemini – June, Virgo – September, Sagittarius – December.* Fill in the other months.

Show the Earth's motion in each of the seasons. Label one of the maps "Spring." Draw the Earth on its orbit opposite the Sun from Pisces. Draw an arrow from the Earth to the Sun and extend it toward Pisces. This shows the Sun's apparent position on the ecliptic on the vernal equinox. Repeat for the months of April and May, and show the Earth's counterclockwise motion around the Sun. Repeat the above for all four seasons.

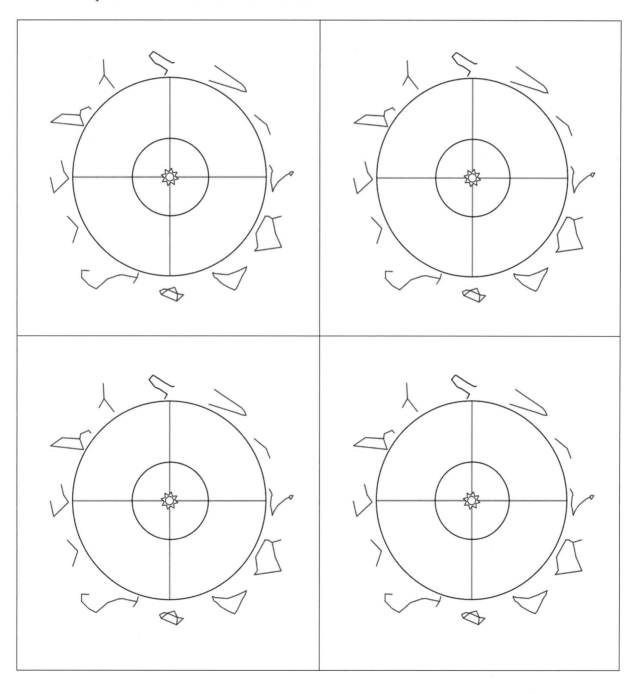

Observing Activities

Sunrise and Sunset

If you have a clear horizon to the east or west, observe the rising or setting of the Sun over the span of a year. (Use the rise and set times from the Research Activity above, or any other weather news source, such as the newspaper, TV weather report, or a weather page on the Internet at Yahoo, MSN, AOL, or Weather.com.) Check about once a week, and record the date and time of sunrise or sunset. Standing in your backyard compass, note the direction of the sunrise or sunset with respect to the eight points of your compass.

Date	Sunrise/ Sunset	Direction	Date	Sunrise/ Sunset	Direction

Notice the seasonal changes in the direction of the sunrise and sunset. If you don't have a clear horizon, observe and record the first appearance of the Sun from behind ground objects. Be sure to not look directly at the Sun, but instead observe the shadows. Make a single sketch below that shows the Sun's different rising or setting compass positions along the horizon at about weekly intervals between the solstices. Draw your Suns small and label them with the date. Note that the Sun's position changes rapidly around the equinoxes and slowly around the solstices. Compare these observations with the amount of daylight for these periods, from your table above.

Exposures

Following the activity in Chapter 1, observe the changes in the direction of sunlight through your windows over the seasons. Notice where the sunlight lands on the walls and floors in the rooms of your house. Pick a place (maybe where you work) and observe the position of the Sun's rays at the same time each day. Put a piece of masking tape along the edge of the sunlight to indicate the position of the rays. Write the date and time on the tape. Note the changes in the rays over a period of weeks and months. Record your observations.

_____

_____

_____

_____

Observing Equinoxes and Solstices

Note the rising and setting Sun between the equinox and its northern or southern extremes on the solstice. If you have access to a street having a clear horizon that runs east to west, watch the Sun rise and set over the ends of the street on the equinox. Also, note that in the days and weeks before and after the equinox, the Sun can be seen rising and setting to the north or south of these directions.

_____

_____

_____

_____

Observing Shadows Due East and Due West

During the spring and summer, note the time of day when the Sun passes above the due east and due west horizons, when the shadows point to the opposite horizon. From your backyard compass, measure the lengths of shadows at these times as compared to the object. For example, measure the length of a stick or the height of a person, and divide the length of the shadow S_L by the length of the object O_L to find a percentage. For example, if the shadow is twice as long as the object, the percentage is 200%. Record this once a week over the spring and summer.

Date	Height of Object	Length of Shadow	Percentage (S_L / O_L)

Finding Your Local High Noon

As we've seen, with our modern systems of Standard Time and Daylight Savings Time, 12:00 PM as read from a clock is somewhat different from "High Noon," when the Sun is at the meridian, and sundials read Noon. Daylight Savings Time is from March to November, and High Noon occurs closer to 1:00 PM rather than 12:00 PM.

Because of Standard Time, "Local Noon" at most locations consistently varies by as much as a half-hour or more, depending on where you live in your time zone. Within each time zone, Standard time is taken from the local time of the time zone meridian. The time zone meridians are at longitudes 15 degrees apart. In the United States, the meridians are as follows:

> *75 degrees west – Eastern Standard Time*
> *90 degrees west – Central Standard Time*
> *105 degrees west – Mountain Standard Time*
> *120 degrees west – Pacific Standard Time*

You can find the correction for your local time to Standard Time by counting four minutes difference for each degree of longitude of your hometown from your time zone meridian. If you live in the western part of your time zone, add four minutes for each degree from the meridian. If you live in the eastern part of your time zone, subtract four minutes for each degree from the meridian.

For example, Cleveland, Ohio is at a longitude of about 82 degrees, seven degrees west of the Eastern time zone meridian. So the Sun reaches High Noon in Cleveland at about 12:28 PM, or about 1:28 PM during Daylight Savings.

(There is still another correction for "sundial time" called *The Equation of Time*, which can vary the time of High Noon by as much as another 20 minutes. We'll learn more about this in a later volume of this series.)

* Using a map, find your longitude. Do you live east or west from your time zone meridian? Find the correction for your local time to Standard Time and record this data in the table below. Use your backyard compass to confirm that the Sun reaches High Noon at more or less your calculated time.

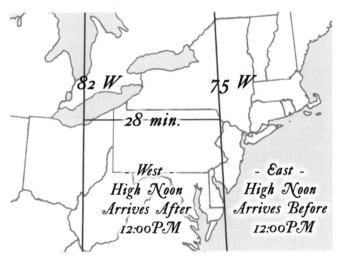

* Using a standard map or road atlas, find the longitudes of several cities in your time zone. Calculate the local noon correction these cities. For example, in the Eastern time zone of the USA, compare: Bangor, Maine; Philadelphia, Pennsylvania; and Grand Rapids, Michigan. Record the local noon corrections and High Noon times in the table on the next page.

* Using your standard map or road atlas, find the longitudes of several cities in two other time zones. Calculate the local noon correction for these cities. Record the local noon corrections and High Noon times for these cities in the tables on the next page.

Your Time Zone Meridian:				
City	Longitude	Dgrs. from Meridian	Local Noon Correction	High Noon Time

Time Zone Meridian:				
City	Longitude	Dgrs. from Meridian	Local Noon Correction	High Noon Time

Time Zone Meridian:				
City	Longitude	Dgrs. from Meridian	Local Noon Correction	High Noon Time

Noon Shadow Activity

At High Noon, measure the lengths of the Noon shadows. Write down your High Noon times from the previous Research Activity. Measure an object and its shadow, such as a stick or a person. As in the previous activity, divide the length of the shadow S_L by the length of the object casting the shadow O_L, to get a percentage of the shadow length (as in the previous activity). Repeat these shadow measurements at weekly intervals from solstice to solstice and record this data on the table below.

Date	High Noon	Height of Object	Length of Shadow	Percentage (S_L / O_L)

Lag of the Seasons Activity

Keep a Temperature Record over the span of the seasons.

Record daily high and low temperatures over the course of the summer or winter seasons. Read the temperatures from a home thermometer, or else collect the official local temperature data from the newspaper or television news. Make a graph that shows daytime high temperatures over your period of measurement. Note when the warmest and coolest periods were as compared with the solstices and equinoxes. (The chart below has enough range to accommodate Fahrenheit and Celsius scales for climates from Texas summers through Alaska winters.)

120°											
110°											
100°											
90°											
80°											
70°											
60°											
50°											
40°											
30°											
20°											
10°											
0°											
-10°											
-20°											
-30°											
-40°											
-50°											
Week											
Month											

Globe Activities

Heliocentric Globe Activity

On manila folders, draw the pattern of each zodiac constellation as shown in Chapters 4 & 5. Make these constellation signs so the "up" end of each constellation is toward the fold. Set up these folders outdoors in a big circle, at least 30 feet (or 9 m). Start with setting up the solstices and equinoxes at the quarter points. Set up the other constellations in between.

Put a lamp in the center of the circle. Use a work light with an extension cord, or a portable gas lantern, etc. Set up your globe opposite the "Sun" from the sign for Gemini. Set the axis of globe so that it "leans" toward the Sun and Gemini. (12 inch world globes typically have a stand that is inclined just like the Earth's axis.)

With the North Pole of the globe inclined toward the Sun and Gemini, note the terminator on the globe. The North Pole is in full light, and most of the northern hemisphere is in the light. Note that the entire South Pole and most of the southern hemisphere is in darkness.

Move the "Earth" counterclockwise around the "Sun" to Autumn, keeping the globe's axis pointed in the same general direction, so that the lamp is aligned with the sign for Virgo. Repeat the above observations. Repeat for each season. Demonstrate this for a friend or family member to help them understand Classical Astronomy.

Geocentric Globe Activity
Using the globe and the light, demonstrate why the Sun appears higher in the sky in the Summer than in Winter. Set up your constellation signs at different heights, outside in a big circle. Maybe Gemini can be set on a step ladder, Sagittarius can be set on the ground, and the Equinoxes on chairs at a height in between the extremes.

Set the globe on a chair in the middle of the circle, with the globe axis pointed straight up. Move your lamp in front of these constellations. Put a paper "stickman" on the globe at your location. Note the variations in the orientation of the terminator on the globe with the "Sun" at these different heights, over the "seasons." As above, show this to another person to help them understand why the Sun appears to rise and fall over the seasons.

Celestial Globe Activity
Use your celestial globe from previous chapters, and the Sun stickers as in the previous activity. Place "Suns" on each of the equinoxes and the solstices, and other points in between. Place your fingers at the "poles" of your globe and rotate it. Notice how the rotation of the Sun varies at each of the seasonal points.

Orion-Constellation Volvelle Activity
Modify your Orion-Constellation volvelle to illustrate the Sun's motion along the Ecliptic.
As with other volvelle activities, dismantle your volvelle or make new cardstock copies of the Orion Base Circle and Orion Horizon. Cut out or make a cardstock copy of the Constellation Wheel from page 113 of the Volvelle Section. Substitute the Constellation Wheel for the Zodiac Wheel from Chapter 4. The months around the periphery of the Constellation Wheel will be used to indicate position of the Sun among the zodiac constellations for the selected month, as explained in detail below.

In the indicated space on your Orion Horizon piece, write the correction for local time calculated

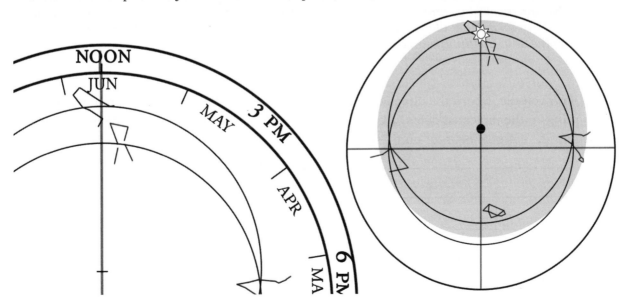

in the previous activity. This will help you make more accurate time estimates for your volvelle. Locate the Sun Position Wheel on page 115 in the Volvelle Section. Make a copy of this wheel onto **transparency material,** e.g. acetate as used for overhead projectors. Cut out the Sun Position Wheel and punch a hole through the center. Take great care to not rip the transparency mateial. Reinforce the center by either applying some clear tape to both sides over the center point, or else by using page reinforcers. Assemble your volvelle so that the transparency sheet is above the Constellation Wheel.

Using Your Volvelle
*   Use the Sun Wheel as an "hour hand" for finding the orientation of the sky for any desired date and time. Point the Sun to the desired date and then rotate the Sun Wheel together with the Constellation Wheel so that the Sun also points to the desired time. Your volvelle will then show the position of the Sun and the constellations above the horizon at that particular date and time.

*   Practice using your modified volvelle. Rotate the Sun Position Wheel so that the Sun points to the vernal equinox (i.e. March 21). Turn the Sun Position Wheel together with the Constellation Wheel to show how the Sun rises and sets on the vernal equinox. Note the directions where the Sun rises and sets.

*   Turn the Sun Position Wheel to the next month, April, and repeat the above. Note the Sun rising and setting further to the north. Repeat for each month of the year. Notice how the rising and setting varies to the north and south over the seasons. Also note how the Sun is progressively higher and lower at the meridian as it moves through the constellations.

*   As you rotate the Sun through the hours of a selected day, note the progression of zodiac constellations that cross the meridian during each hour. As you move the Sun into the nighttime hours, notice which constellations are visible at each hour of the night. Compare your volvelle with the actual night sky. After dark on a clear night, set the Sun Position Wheel to your current date. Turn the Sun Position Wheel and Constellation Wheel to the current hour and note the zodiac constellation indicated at the volvelle meridian for that time. Be sure to take into account daylight savings and your correction for local time. Confirm from your backyard compass whether that constellation is actually at the meridian over the southern horizon. Use your volvelle in this way to find the constellations on any clear night of the year.

N.B: *Even though hours have been placed around the outer edge, a flat volvelle cannot correctly imitate the spherical sky, and will not give precisely accurate hour readings. However, your volvelle will approximately illustrate the progression of the celestial bodies and many interesting aspects of the sky. Confirm your volvelle readings with actual observations.*

Using your volvelle, record the directions on the horizon where the Sun can be found while rising and setting on the indicated dates. Also record where the Sun can be found at the meridian with respect to the celestial equator on these dates.

Direction	March 21	June 21	September 23	December 21
Rising				
Setting				
Meridian				

Find the times of Sunrise, Sunset, High Noon and Hours of Daylight
Use your Orion-Constellation volvelle to find the times of sunrise, High Noon, and sunset for your location for each of the indicated dates. Be sure to add the correction for local time and also an hour for daylight savings during the specific months. Add up the hours to find the length of daylight for each date. Find this by counting the hours between sunrise and 12:00 P.M., and from between 12:00 P.M. and sunset.

As Measured From Your Volvelle				
Date	Sunrise	High Noon	Sunset	Hrs. Daylight
January 21				
February 21				
March 21				
April 21				
Mar 21				
June 21				
July 21				
August 21				
September 23				
October 21				
November 21				
December 21				

N.B.: *As mentioned above, your volvelle is only a greatly simplified tool for simulating the motions of the celestial bodies. The volvelle itself is a "flattened" representation of the spherical sky, and does not accurately represent the real sky as we see it. As a further factor, the horizon piece has been made to roughly approximate the horizon as seen from the latitude 40 North. It will roughly correspond to the horizons for most of North America and Europe, but will not represent the horizon of the Arctic region or the southernmost United Statess.*

Also, as a generalized model of the actual sky, the volvelle neglects many astronomical variables such as the elliptical orbit of the Earth. Because of this and several other factors, you can only take an "eyeball" reading from your volvelle, and this leaves much room for personal interpretation when taking readings.

Margin of Error in Your Volvelle

In the table below, record the sunrise and sunset times read from your volvelle in the previous section. Record the actual times of sunrise and sunset for the indicated dates at your location as found from an authoritative source, such as an astronomical almanac or available online from the U.S. Naval Observatory *Complete Sun and Moon Data for One Day* web site.

Compare these times by calculating their differences. Subtract the actual sunrise from your volvelle readings, and indicate that time as a positive or negative number in the table below.

Date	Sunrise (Volvelle)	Sunrise (Actual)	Difference	Sunset (Volvelle)	Sunset (Actual)	Difference
January 21						
February 21						
March 21						
April 21						
Mar 21						
June 21						
July 21						
August 21						
September 23						
October 21						
November 21						
December 21						

Your volvelle readings should be roughly within 10 or 15 minutes of the actual times. But all things considered, this isn't really too bad for some hand-cut paper circles!

Field Activities for Chapter 6
The Seasonal Skies

Sketching, Flat Map and Celestial Globe Activities

Referring to the constellations shown in Chapter 6, sketch the skies of each season in the spaces below, and label the bright first magnitude stars. Become familiar with these star patterns. This will help you in finding the constellations in the sky.

The Winter Sky	*The Spring Sky*
The Summer Sky	*The Autumn Sky*

Add the aforementioned constellations to your celestial globe and also the flat map on the next page. For your flat map, be sure to sketch them in with pencil. Once you have all the stars added in the way you like, draw over them in ink, so you can make clean photocopies (which will help in Chapter 7).

Solar System Map Activity

Refer to the solar system maps made in the previous section to represent each season. Note the constellations that are in the opposite direction from the Sun during each month of the year. These constellations rise as the Sun sets. Fill in the table below to indicate the month, the constellation hosting the Sun during that month, and the opposite constellation. For your current month, confirm from your observations whether this constellation is rising in the east during the evening after the Sun has set, and reaches the meridian at midnight.

Month	*Constellation Hosting the Sun*	*Opposite Constellation*	*Rising in the Evening?*	*At Meridian at Midnight?*

Find Your Limiting Magnitude

Determine the "limiting magnitude" of your local sky, the magnitude of the faintest star visible. Knowing your limiting magnitude will help you determine whether or not the faint constellations such as Pisces and Capricornus can be seen from locations in the city or suburbs. The Little Dipper is an excellent indicator, since the bowl and handle include faint stars of fourth and fifth magnitude. Consult the picture on the second page of Chapter 6 for a guide. If you are in a rural location with the Milky Way overhead, your sky is magnitude 5 or better, and you should have no problem seeing the faint stars.

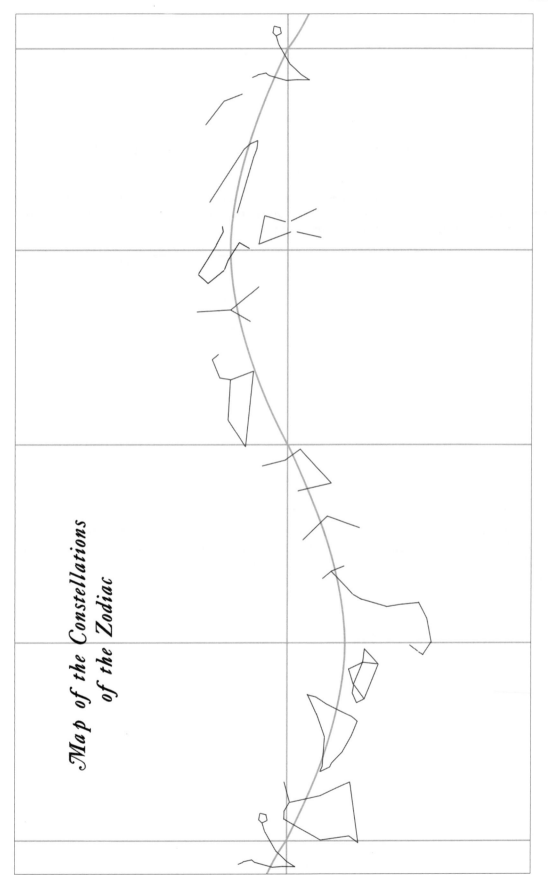

Map of the Constellations
of the Zodiac

Observing the Zodiac

In late evening twilight, observe the zodiac constellation in the western sky above the place of the sunset. Sketch what you see, recording the date and time and direction. Does this confirm the Sun's position on the Ecliptic for your current month?

Calculate the time of your local "astronomical midnight." Count the hours and minutes between sunset and sunrise, divide by two, and subtract that number of hours from the time of sunrise. Go out and observe the sky at that time and note the zodiac constellation at the meridian at local midnight. Confirm whether this constellation is directly opposite in the sky from the place of the sun.

Observe the zodiac constellation above the eastern horizon in early morning twilight before the sunrise. Sketch and record what you see. Does this also confirm the Sun's position on the ecliptic, as found in the evening and at midnight?

Evening	*Midnight*	*Morning*
Constellation:		
Date & Time:		

Continue to observe the western sky in late evening twilight at least once a week for three months. Notice how the zodiac constellations disappear into the sunset over a period of time. Similarly, observe the eastern sky before sunrise during the same period and observe the zodiac constellations emerging from the sunrise. Repeat the above activity at one-month intervals and sketch and record your results in the panels below.

Evening	*Midnight*	*Morning*
Constellation:		
Date & Time:		

Evening	*Midnight*	*Morning*
Constellation:		
Date & Time:		

Evening	*Midnight*	*Morning*
Constellation:		
Date & Time:		

Observe the First Magnitude Stars

Consulting the star map pictures in Chapter 6 and the table in the Appendix, note the positions of the fifteen first magnitude stars as compared to the zodiac constellations. Make a table of the first magnitude stars. Indicate whether any of these stars are included in a zodiac constellation or whether the zodiac constellations are directly north or south of these bright stars. This will help you find which first magnitude stars reach the meridian with the zodiac constellations.

Star	*Constellation*	*Position*		*Star*	*Constellation*	*Position*

In the table below, identify the names of the first magnitude stars and their constellations. Using the information from the previous table and referring to the zodiac table in the Appendix, record the times when each of the first magnitude stars are near the meridian during your current month. Observe the stars visible in the evening an hour after sunset and an hour before sunrise. Indicate their position, whether any are high in the sky near your zenith or whether they are low in the sky.

Date	1ˢᵗ Mag. Star	Constellation	Meridian Times	AM or PM?	Position at Meridian

Consulting the constellation patterns shown in Chapter 6, list the constellations that can be seen in your current evening sky. Observe the sky to determine which constellations are to the east and to the west of the meridian. Use the reverse compass from Chapter 2 to properly navigate around the sky. For each constellation, indicate the directions to the nearby constellations. For example, Orion is south of Gemini, and northwest of Canis Major.

Date/Time	Constellation	Meridian – E or W?	Nearby Constellations	Directions to

Find Vega and Capella

These bright stars lie quite far to the north, and at least one is always visible above the horizon from each state in the USA and the latitudes further to the north. As a matter of fact, these stars are within the "always visible" circle as seen from the latitude of London and beyond! Vega and Capella can be found from their positions as compared to the Big Dipper and Cassiopeia. Learn to identify these stars, and find their neighboring constellations. Sketch and record two observations of these stars at different dates and times.

Refer to the list of bright stars you observed in the meridian activity of Chapter 2. Can you now identify any of these bright stars? If so, record the star names and constellations. Otherwise, try to determine which stars they might be from the dates and times of their observations. Use your volvelle as modified below to help you make this determination.

Date/Time	Star Name	Constellation		Date/Time	Star Name	Constellation

Observe the Northern Sky

On one evening each week, observe the Big Dipper and Cassiopeia at the same time, e.g. 10:00 PM. Once a month, sketch the orientation of these stars as they appear at that hour. Note the progression over the span of four months.

Date/Time:	*Date/Time:*
Date/Time:	*Date/Time:*

Cassiopeia lies amidst the Milky Way at its northernmost extent, and can help you visualize the connection between the summer and winter skies. Under a dark sky, if you can see the neighborhood of Orion, follow the Milky Way north past Capella to Cassiopeia and continue back again toward the horizon. Imagine the place of the Summer Triangle somewhere below the horizon. And if the Summer Triangle is in the sky, follow the Milky Way past Vega to Cassiopeia and down to the northern horizon. Imagine Orion and friends invisibly below the northern horizon.

Observe Orion

Use the Appendix in *Signs & Seasons* to find the time for observing Orion in your current month. Note the position in the sky. Observe Orion once a week at the same time. Sketch the progression of Orion across the sky over a span of three months. Include the compass points, height above the horizon, and orientation of Orion in the sky. If Orion is not visible in the current season, select a different constellation.

Month 1:	*Month 2:*	*Month 3:*

Visual Acuity Activity

Pleiades – Being able to count six stars in the Pleiades is a great test of eyesight. Sharp eyes can easily pick out all six. Nearsighted eyes may see the brighter stars clearly, but not all. To some eyes (like the author's!) the Pleiades look like a fuzzy blob. Observe the Pleiades with your whole family or other group of people. See how many Pleiades stars each person can count.

Mizar – Big Dipper – The star Mizar is at the "bend in the handle" of the Big Dipper. This star has a companion star named Alcor, and sharp eyes can easily spot two stars instead of one. However, those with nearsighted vision can only spot one star. Have your group spot Mizar and Alcor to determine who can see two stars rather than only one.

Name	*Pleiades – Number of Stars*	*Mizar – Number of Stars*

Use binoculars or a telescope to find *deep sky objects* such as galaxies and nebulae. Find the *Andromeda Galaxy* as shown in Chapter 6. Also, look for the famous *Orion Nebula* in the Sword of Orion. There is a prominent *globular cluster* in Hercules, to the south of the northwest star in the Keystone. We'll learn more about the deep sky in a later volume of this series.

Globe Activity

This is a follow-up to the "seasonal" globe activity from Chapter 5. Use your globe and your "geocentric" constellation setup to demonstrate the constellations visible in the evening, at midnight and in the morning. Set your globe in the center with the Zodiac constellation signs arranged around it in a circle. Place a lamp for the Sun in front of the constellation for the Spring. Tape your "stickman" onto the globe to represent your location on the Earth.

* Turn the globe so that your stickman is on the sunset terminator. Note the constellation opposite the Sun. Note the constellation in between, representing the stars at the meridian in evening twilight.

* Turn the globe to the "midnight" position. Note that stickman is facing the constellation opposite the Sun, which corresponds to the stars at meridian at midnight. Turn the globe so stickman is on the "sunrise" terminator. Note the arrangement of the constellations from this perspective.

* Repeat the above for each season. Repeat the activity using the softball to show the positions of the moon's phases.

Volvelle Activities

Label stars on your Orion-Constellation volvelle

As space permits, label the first magnitude stars indicated as small circles on the Constellation Wheel of your Orion-Constellation volvelle. Be sure to write small so as to not clutter up the volvelle. If you wish, indicate the constellations in which these stars reside. Experiment with your volvelle to discover interesting information about the Sun and stars.

Find Orion in All Seasons

Turn your constellation wheel so that Orion is in the east. Turn the Sun to line up with different months around the dial. Observe the Sun's position and note the time of day when Orion is rising for each month of the year. Record these results in the table on the next page. Repeat the above for when Orion is at the meridian and western horizon.

Month	Orion Rising	Orion at Meridian	Orion Setting
January			
February			
March			
April			
May			
June			
July			
August			
September			
October			
November			
December			

Find the First Magnitude Stars

Use your volvelle to estimate when the first magnitude stars will be near the meridian. To find out when Arcturus will be near the meridian on a certain date, turn your Sun to the desired day of the month. Then turn the Sun and the constellation wheel together until Arcturus is at the meridian. Note the hour on the Base Circle at which the Sun is pointed, and take daylight savings and local time into account. Is the Sun still in the sky at that hour? If so, Arcturus cannot be seen at the meridian. But if the Sun is down, you can find Arcturus if you look at that hour! Using your volvelle, estimate the hour of the day when the first magnitude stars cross the meridian during the indicated months. Record your results in the tables below.

Month	Names of the First Magnitude Stars				
January					
February					
March					
April					
May					
June					
July					
August					
September					
October					
November					
December					

Month	Names of the First Magnitude Stars				
January					
February					
March					
April					
May					
June					
July					
August					
September					
October					
November					
December					

Month	*Names of the First Magnitude Stars*				
January					
February					
March					
April					
May					
June					
July					
August					
September					
October					
November					
December					

Find the Zodiac Constellations at the Meridian

Using your volvelle, find the zodiac constellations at the meridian at these times: in the evening one hour after sunset; at midnight; and in the morning one hour before sunrise. Repeat this for the same date for each month of the year. Record your results in the table below.

Month	*Zodiac Constellations*		
	After Sunset	*Midnight*	*Before Sunrise*
January			
February			
March			
April			
May			
June			
July			
August			
September			
October			
November			
December			

Modify your Northern Sky Volvelle

As with other volvelle activities, either dismantle your Northern Sky Volvelle or make another copy of the Base Circle and Horizon piece. Cut out or make a cardstock copy of the "dark sky" Northern Stars Wheel from page 117 in the Volvelle Section. Substitute this wheel for the previous one. Use the months on this wheel to find any orientation of the Big Dipper and Cassiopeia for any hour of the day, any day of the year! Find the orientation of the northern sky by lining up the desired month with the desired time. Unlike your other volvelles, the modified Northern Sky Volvelle will show an accurate sky for any time of day, for any day of the year. Be sure to take into account daylight savings and your local time correction for standard time.

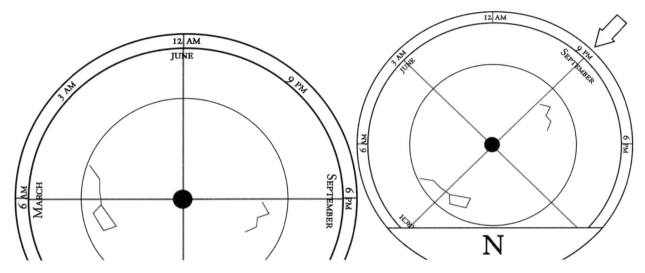

*   Turn the wheel so that it aligns with your current month and the time of evening twilight. Observe the northern sky at this time. Does your volvelle agree with your observation? Repeat for midnight and morning twilight, and observe the sky at these times.

Positions of the Northern Constellations

Use your volvelle to find the orientation of the sky for any night of the year. Use the table below to record the hours of the day when the Big Dipper is at the indicated positions for each month.

Month	Above Polaris	West of Polaris	Below Polaris	East of Polaris
January				
February				
March				
April				
May				
June				
July				
August				
September				
October				
November				
December				

Vega and Capella

Note that the "dark sky" wheel includes Vega and Cappella. These stars are roughly "in between" the Big Dipper and Cassiopeia, not far from the perpendicular line that intersects these two constellations. The orientation of the Big Dipper and Cassiopeia can be used to help locate these stars when they are low in the northern sky, after their risings and before their settings.

Rotate your volvelle so that Vega and Capella are at the same elevation above the horizon, with Vega in the northeast and Capella is in the northwest. Read off your volvelle the hour of the day for each month when these stars are in this position. Rotate your volvelle so that Vega in the northwest and Capella is in the northeast and read off the hour of days when these stars are in this position for each month. Use the table below to record these hours for each of these positions. Observe these stars at each of these positions during the current month.

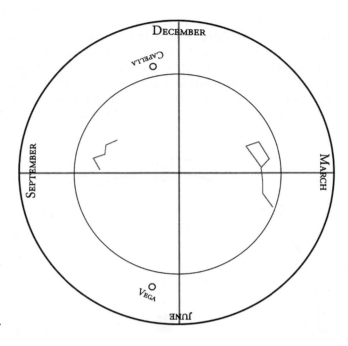

Month	Vega Northwest - Capella Northeast	Capella Northwest - Vega Northeast
January		
February		
March		
April		
May		
June		
July		
August		
September		
October		
November		
December		

Compare with your constellation volvelle, and use these two together to become aquainted with the appearance of the sky at different dates and times. If you like volvelles and would like to make more different types, check out the *Paper Plate Education* web site:

http://analyzer.depaul.edu/paperplate/

Field Activities for Chapter 7
The Wandering Stars

Solar System Map Activity

Use the solar system maps below and consult the table in the Appendix of *Signs & Seasons*. Draw the opposition positions for the superior planets for all the years indicated in the appendix. Indicate the planet at that position on its orbital circle, in front of the appropriate constellation, and label the year. Indicate the orbital position of Earth on those dates and include these dates on the map. Do the same for Venus, except indicate the positions at inferior conjunction. Note any patterns or recurring cycles that you observe with the orbits of the planets. *(Note - the orbits of Venus and Mars are shown to scale, but the orbits of Jupiter and Saturn are not.)*

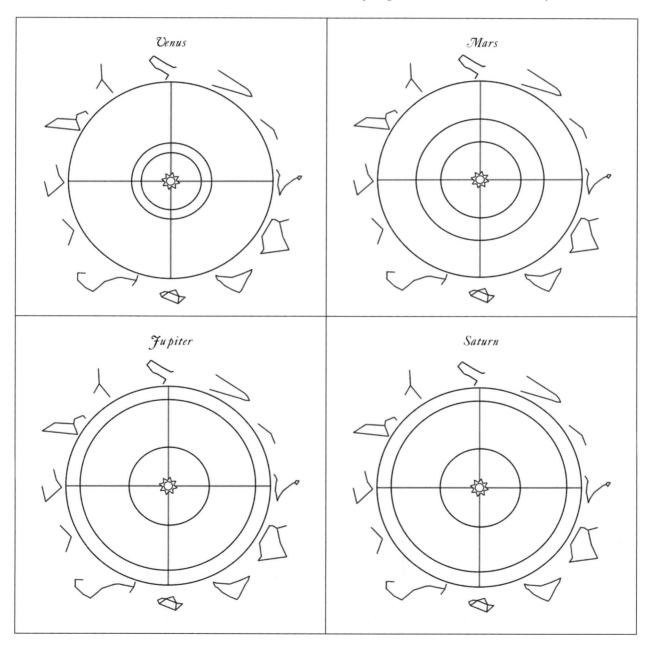

As above, use the solar system maps and consult the Appendix. For the current cycle of Venus, draw the positions of Venus and Earth on their orbital circles to indicate inferior and superior conjunctions, and also maximum eastern and western elongations. Indicate dates and draw lines connecting Venus and Earth for each event. Do the same for the superior planets, indicating superior conjunction, opposition, and eastern and western quadratures (assuming no movement for the superior planets). Note how far the Earth travels in its orbit during these times.

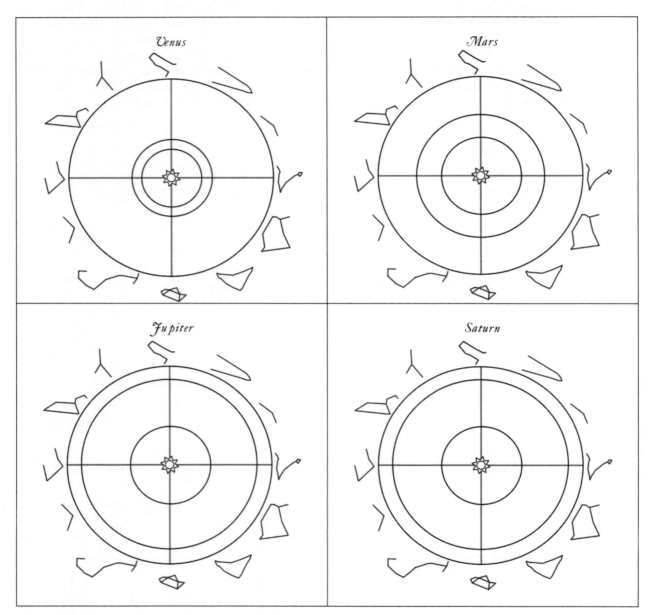

Flat Map Activity

On the following flat map page, draw the opposition positions and dates of each of the superior planets for several consecutive years as given in the Appendix. On the next pages after, draw the positions among the constellations for the Sun and Venus, indicating the conjunctions and maximum elongations, including dates. Include the positions and dates of any of your own observations. Make copies and use them to record this data if your map gets too cluttered.

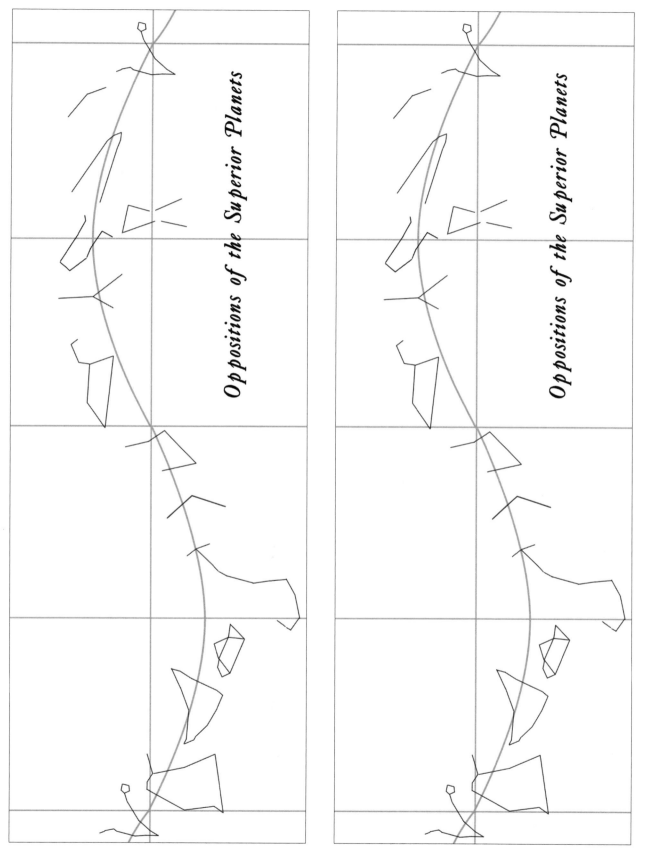

Oppositions of the Superior Planets

Oppositions of the Superior Planets

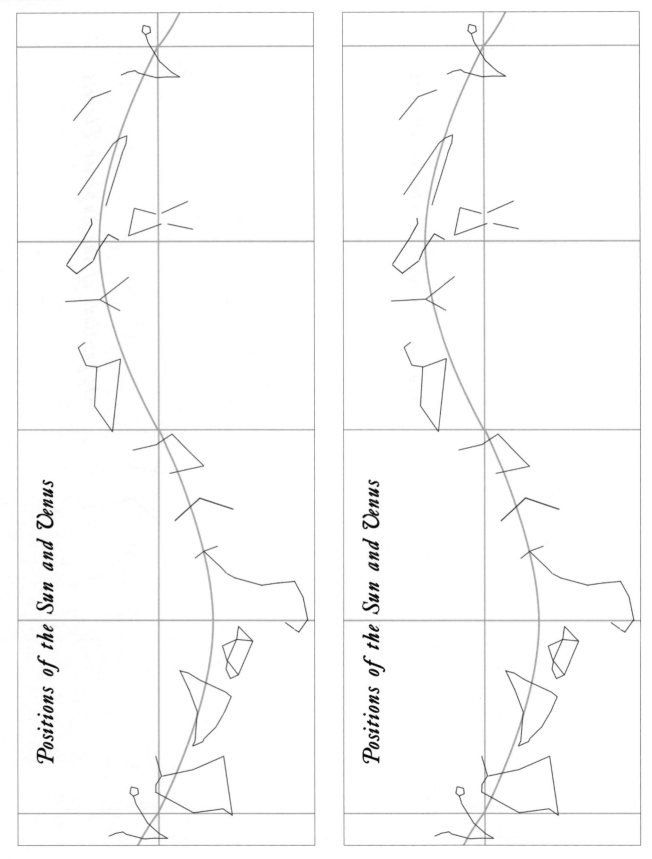

Positions of the Sun and Venus

Positions of the Sun and Venus

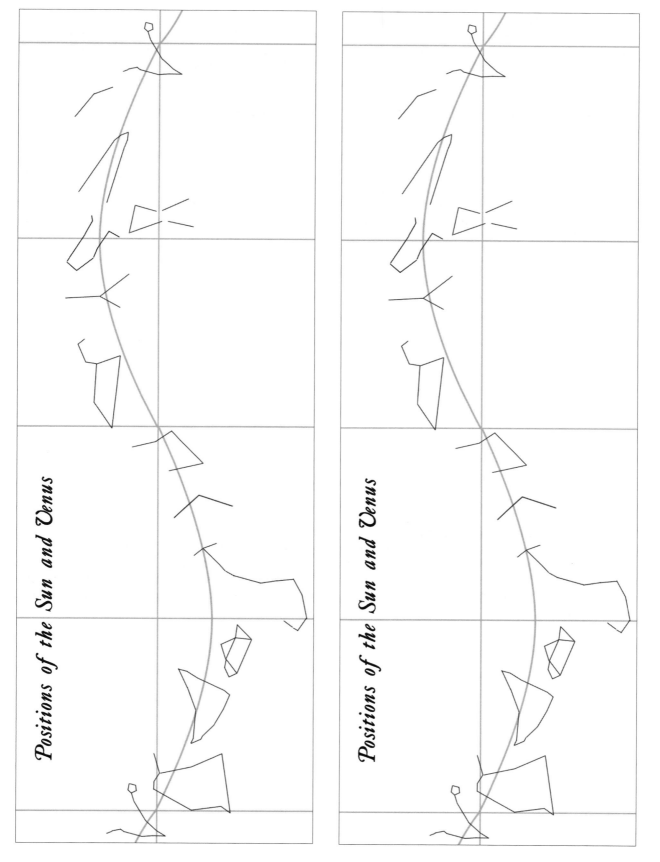

Positions of the Sun and Venus

Positions of the Sun and Venus

Observe Venus

Consult the Appendix to find out whether Venus is currently visible in the morning or the evening. Note the brightness of Venus, how much brighter it is than any other stars. It's easy to understand that UFO sightings always increase when Venus is an evening star!

In the panel below, sketch Venus once a week for three months as it appears in the morning or evening sky. Check Venus in twilight and in the nighttime before or after. Record the date and time of your observations. Note the height of Venus above the horizon and its position with respect to the compass points, along with any ground objects (trees, buildings, utility poles, etc.) Use your reverse compass to show whether Venus's elongation is to the east or west of the Sun. If possible, note the constellation that Venus is currently passing through. Referring to the Appendix, determine if Venus is increasing or decreasing in elongation. Note any changes in height above the horizon and distance from the sunset over the weeks and months. Note that Venus may have a large elongation from the Sun but not be high above the horizon. Can you explain why that happens?

Observe the Superior Planets

Consult the Appendix to find the oppositions of the superior planets. If possible, observe the planets at times around their oppositions. Sketch the position of the planet amidst its constellation, and record the date and time. If an opposition has already occurred for your current year, or if it yet to come, look for the planet at or near the constellation of opposition and sketch what you see.

Mars	*Jupiter*	*Saturn*

Observe the Conjunctions

Moon and Stars

Observe the Moon each month as it passes near one or more of the bright first magnitude stars near the ecliptic – *Aldebaran, Regulus, Spica,* and *Antares*. Depending on the season, observe these conjunctions in the evening or morning. Record the date of each. Record the month and date for each. Under the star name, indicate the Moon phases for that conjunction, e.g. for February, under *Aldebaran,* write *First Quarter*. Note that the phase of the Moon is different from month to month as the Moon passes these stars. (Don't worry if you can't record each conjunction every single month.)

Month	Date	Moon Phase for each Conjunction			
		Aldebaran	Regulus	Spica	Antares
January					
February					
March					
April					
May					
June					
July					
August					
September					
October					
November					
December					

Stars and Planets

As the planets make their way along the zodiac circle, they can pass very close to the bright stars along the ecliptic. Consult the Appendix to see when a planet will be passing through Taurus, Leo, Virgo or Scorpius. Keep on eye on that part of the sky, and where each star column and planet row intersect, record the date when the star and planet make their closest pass.

Conjunctions	Aldebaran	Regulus	Spica	Antares
Venus				
Mars				
Jupiter				
Saturn				

Moon and Planets

As you observe Venus and the superior planets in the previous activities, be sure to note the monthly passages of the Moon, as you did in the aforementioned activity. For each month, record the dates and the phases of each conjunction, as above.

Month	Date	Moon Phase for each Conjunction			
		Venus	Mars	Jupiter	Saturn
January					
February					
March					
April					
May					
June					
July					
August					
September					
October					
November					
December					

Planets and Planets

Conjunctions between two superior planets are less common, but the swifter Mars swings by the slower Jupiter and Saturn with each apparation. Since Jupiter and Saturn move very slowly, these planets come into conjunction with Venus when they are closer to the sunrise or sunset. As you observe the planets, take note if they are drawing near other planets. Sketch and record any planetary conjunctions that you observe, with time and date. For the superior planets, look in the Appendix and note the year when two superior planets will reach opposition in the same constellation.

Conjunctions	Venus	Mars	Jupiter	Saturn
Venus				
Mars				
Jupiter				
Saturn				

Conjunctions of the Moon, stars and planets are frequently reported in the
Classical Astronomy Update - www.ClassicalAstronomy.com!

Observing the Moon Along the Zodiac

Seasonal variations – Observe the thin waxing crescent when it first appears in the evening sky. Using a single panel, sketch the position of the crescent as it changes position from evening to evening. Is it moving more vertically each night or it is moving more horizontally? Note the season and determine which constellations the Moon is passing through. Compare this with what you learned of the zodiac in previous chapters.

Observe the rising of the Full Moon, and also the waning gibbous Moon for about three or four days thereafter. Sketch the Moon at these times including a horizon with ground objects and indicating the directions where the Moon rises, as seen from your backyard compass. Note whether the risings of the Moon change from north to south with each night. Repeat this over a four month period.

Month 1

Month 2

Month 3

Month 4

Over the same four month period, observe the risings of the Full Moon. Using a single panel, sketch the positions of the Full Moon's risings over this period, showing its directions with respect to due east.

Full Moon Rising

For the activity above, observe the Full Moon's risings and determine the constellation in which is rises. In the table below, record the constellations hosting the Full Moon over the four month period. Use this to estimate the Sun's position on the ecliptic during these months.

Month	*List the Constellations Hosting:*	
	The Full Moon	*The Sun*

Using the techniques learned in the moonfinding activity from Chapter 3, determine when the Moon will be transiting the meridian for a one week period.

Date	*Phase*	*Moonrise*	*Moonset*	*Hrs. in the Sky*	*Transit Time*

Using the information in the previous table, observe the Moon's position at these times. Note whether the Moon appears higher or lower than the previous day. Determine whether the Moon is heading north or south through the zodiac, and observe the constellation through which the Moon is moving on that day (estimate the constellation if the Moon is observed during the daytime.)

Date	Phase	Higher or Lower?	Constellation

Observing Moon Shadows

Perform this activity after dark during the waxing gibbous, full, and waning gibbous phases. Measure the lengths of someone's shadows while standing in your backyard compass when the Moon is crossing the meridian. Record the percentages of shadow length S by height H. Note the changes in shadow length from night to night, as the Moon moves from north to south through the constellations.

Date	Moon Phase	Height (H)	Shadow (S)	Percentage (S/H)

In the following table, record the changes of the lengths of the shadows of the Full Moon over a span of four months. List the constellation hosting the Full Moon. Compare these shadow lengths with the meridian lengths of the shadows from the Sun when in the same constellation, as you measured in Chapter 5.

Month	*Full Moon Shadows*	*Constellations*	*Sun Shadows*

As the Moon approaches and passes the meridian, draw a cardinal line using the Moon's shadows.

Half Moon at Meridian (for advanced observers)

Record the appearance of the half-moon at the meridian each month between the solstices. Keep a set of sketches for each month and write the date. Note the Moon's terminator – is it vertically straight or is it inclined? (Note the appearances shown in the book.) Does the tilt of the Moon's terminator change with the seasons? Why would that be? (Hint – compare the constellation of the Moon with the constellation of the Sun, as compared to the Celestial Equator.)

Orion-Constellation Volvelle Activity

As with other volvelle activities, dismantle your Orion-Constellation volvelle or make a new one from cardstock copies. Use the Moon Phase Position Wheel from the *transparency sheet* of page 115. Cut the circle and poke a hole at the center, using tape for reinforcement. Use this wheel instead of the Sun Position Wheel from Chapter 5 in order to locate the phases of the Moon for each month of the year. Assemble your volvelle so that the transparency sheet is on top.

Using Your Volvelle – Consult your wall calendar to find the date of the nearest quarter of the Moon, e.g. New or Full Moon, First or Last Quarter. Set the Sun to that date and note the position of that quarter. Find the Moon's position for that quarter and for the nearby ages of the Moon, waxing or waning and for crescent or gibbous phases.

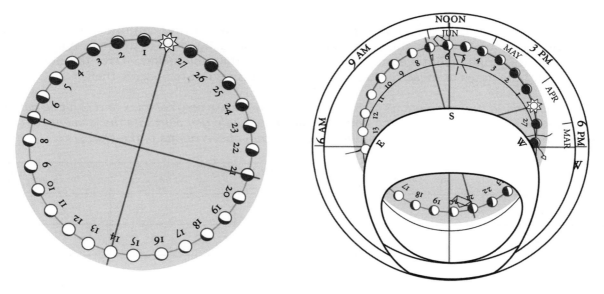

Constellations of the Moon's Quarters

As you dial in the Sun for each month, note the constellations in which the Moon's quarters are seen. Confirm this by observation for the current month. Note that, in any phase, for any month, the Moon rises, crosses the meridian and sets with its host constellation. Use your volvelle to find the constellation hosting the Moon in each quarter, for each month of the year. Record your results in the table below. In the coming months, confirm your findings by observing the Moon in these constellations.

Month	New Moon	First Quarter	Full Moon	Last Quarter
January				
February				
March				
April				
May				
June				
July				
August				
September				
October				
November				
December				

Conjunctions With Planets

Use your volvelle to find the approximate age of the Moon during conjunctions between the Moon and the first magnitude stars near the ecliptic. For each month of the year, note the Moon age nearest the bright ecliptic stars, and record this in the table below. Over the next several months, find the dates of these conjunctions and make an effort to observe them.

N.B.: *Keep in mind that the motions of the Moon and planets are very complex and can't be perfectly modeled on a flat paper volvelle. But your volvelle should help you calculate these events to within a day or two. Confirm your volvelle readings with actual observations of the sky.*

Month	Aldebaran	Regulus	Spica	Antares
January				
February				
March				
April				
May				
June				
July				
August				
September				
October				
November				
December				

*   Use removable planet stickers (usually found in craft stores) to indicate the positions of the planets during any month or season indicated in the tables in the Appendix. Your volvelle will help you find the risings, meridian crossings, and settings of any of these planets. The phases on the Moon Phase Wheel will also help you find the dates and times of conjunctions between the Moon and planets. Record your findings below.

_____

_____

_____

_____

Your volvelle is a simple "analog computer" for finding the positions of the Sun, Moon, stars and planets. Repeat any of the above activities and experiment with your volvelle to estimate interesting celestial events in the coming months and years.

Volvelle Section

Create Rotatable Wheel Calculators that Simulate the Motions of the Sun, Moon and Stars

Please Note:

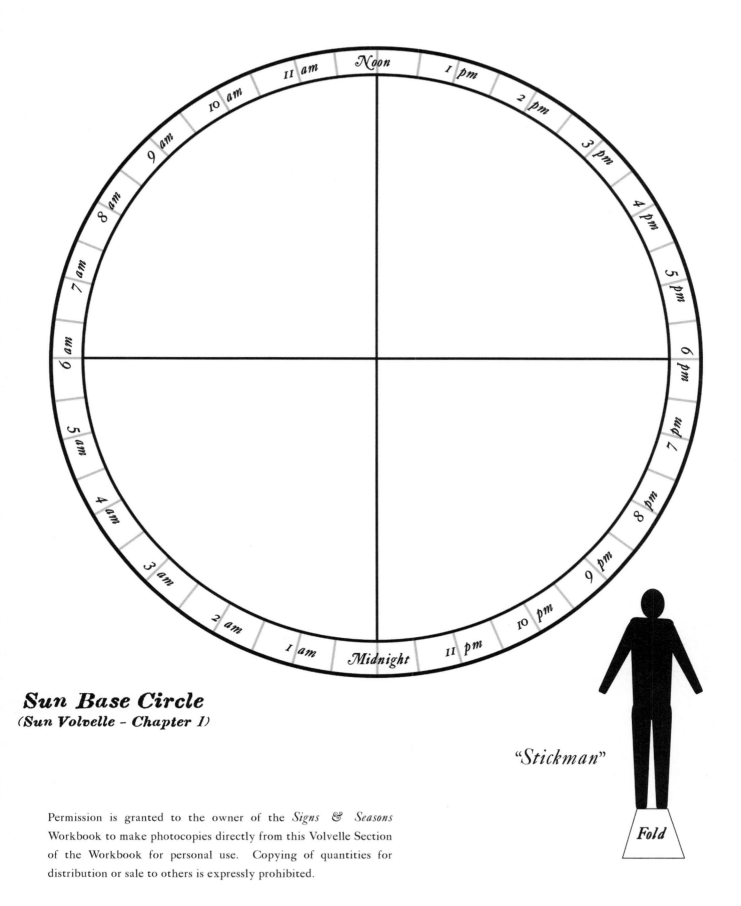

Sun Base Circle
(Sun Volvelle – Chapter 1)

"Stickman"

Fold

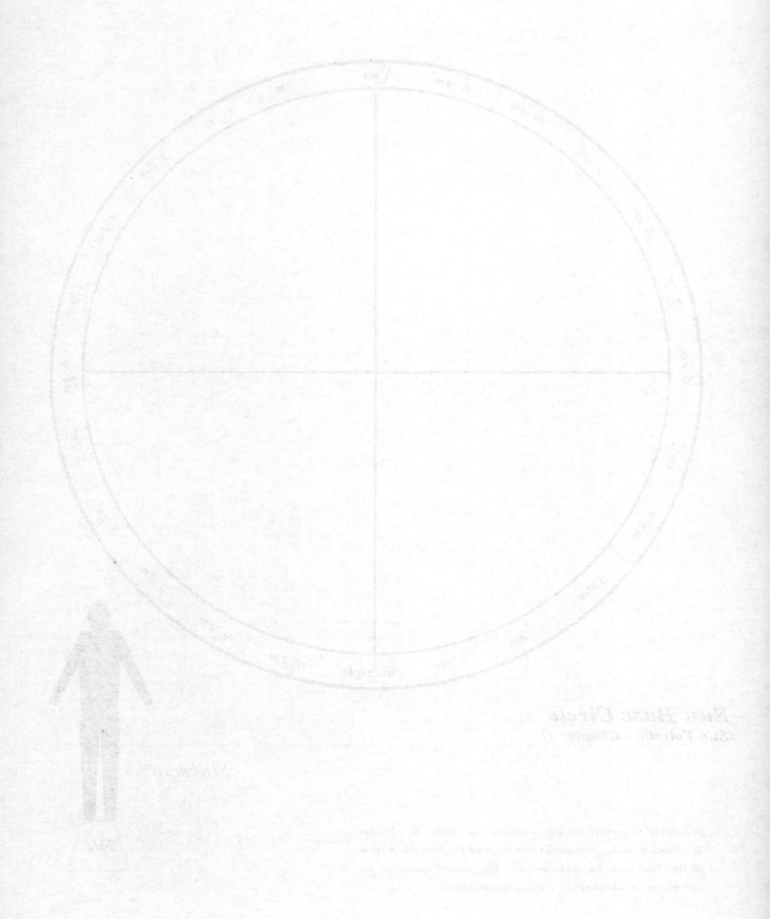

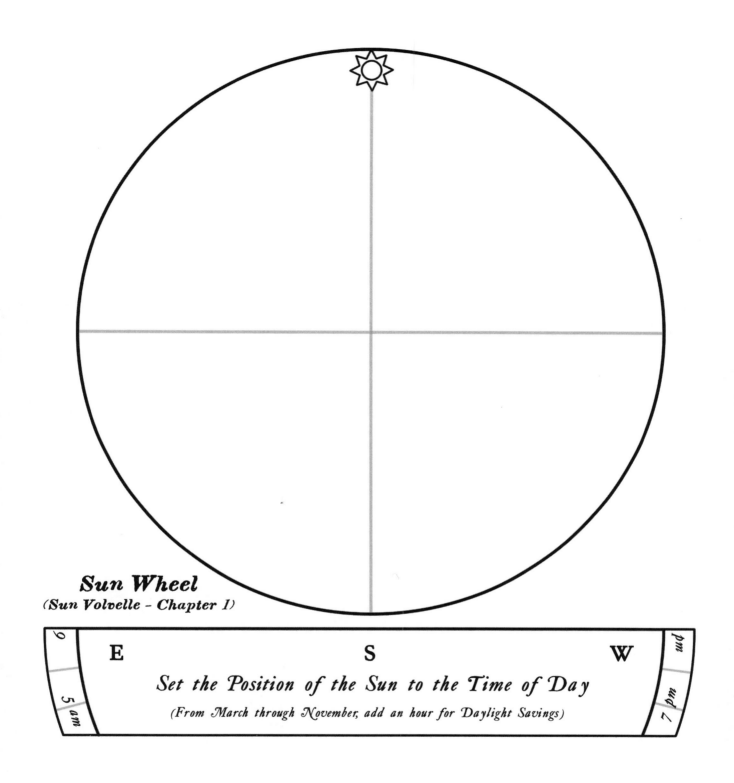

Sun Wheel
(Sun Volvelle - Chapter 1)

E   S   W

9

5 am

pm

7 pm

Set the Position of the Sun to the Time of Day
(From March through November, add an hour for Daylight Savings)

Sun Volvelle Horizon
(Sun Volvelle - Chapter 1)

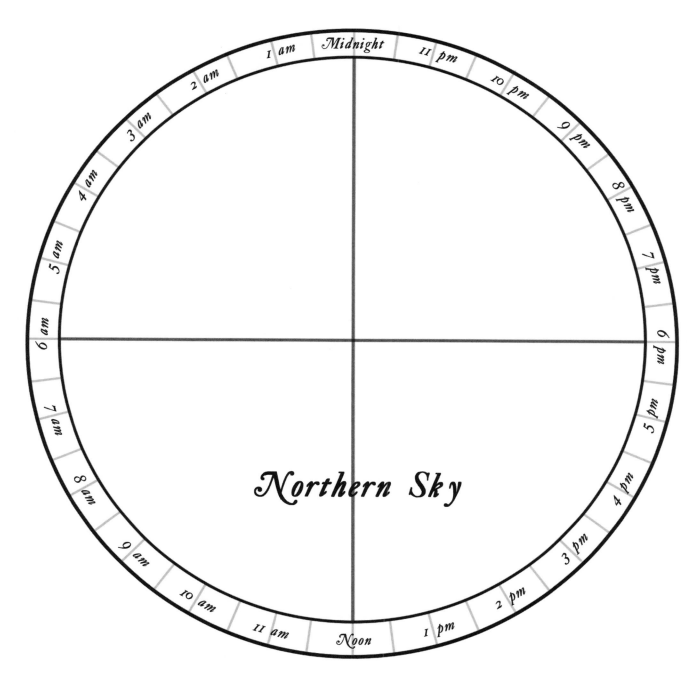

Northern Base Circle
(Northern Stars Volvelle – Chapter 2)

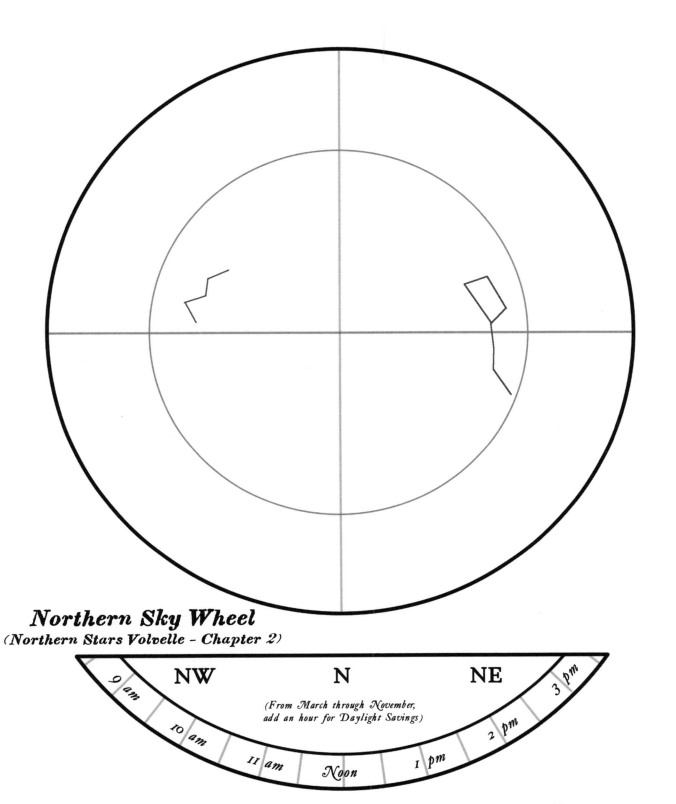

Northern Sky Wheel
(Northern Stars Volvelle - Chapter 2)

9 am **NW** 10 am 11 am **N** Noon 1 pm **NE** 2 pm 3 pm

(From March through November,
add an hour for Daylight Savings)

Northern Horizon
(Northern Stars Volvelle - Chapter 2)

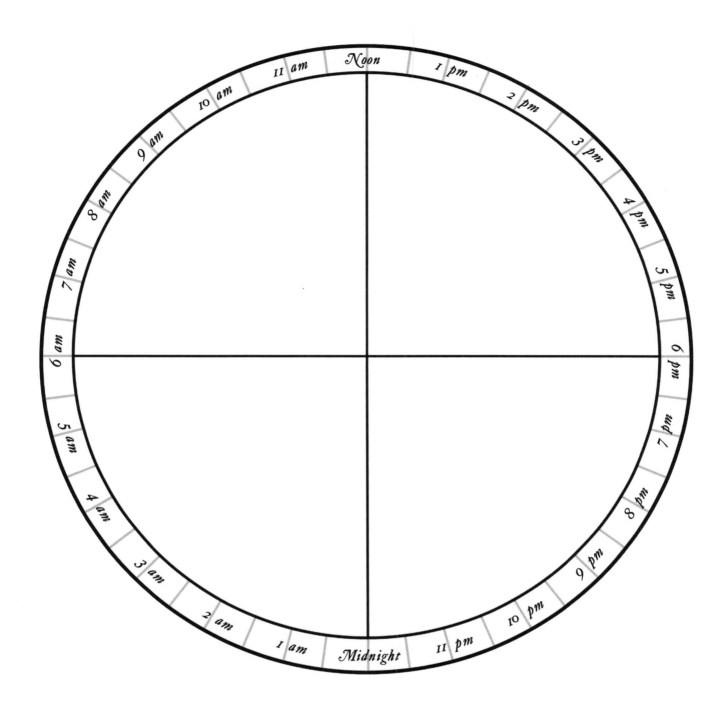

Orion Base Circle
(Orion Volvelle – Chapter 2)

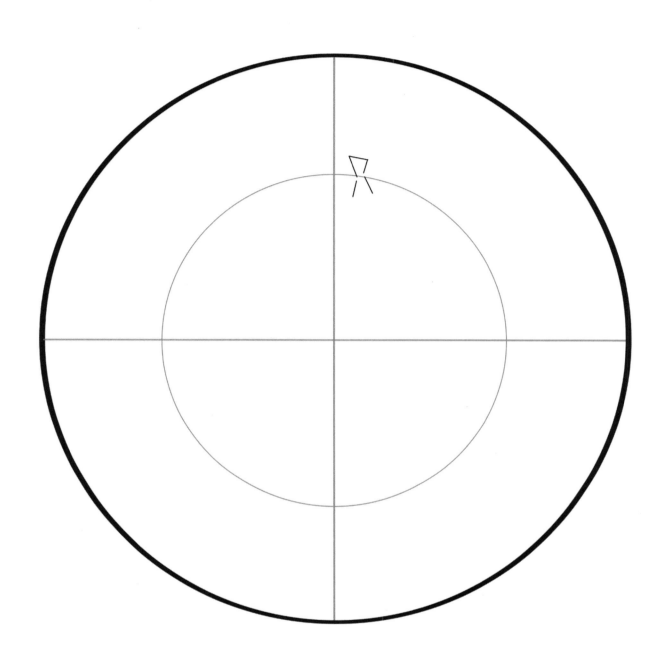

Orion Wheel
(Orion Volvelle – Chapter 2)

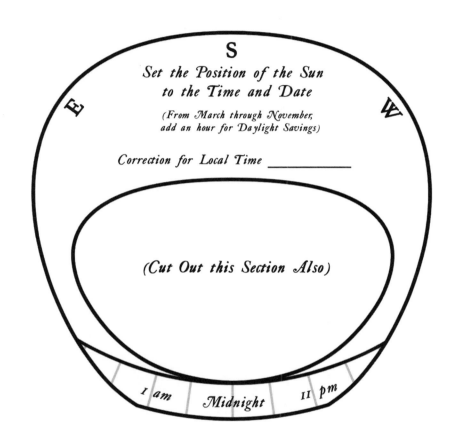

S

*Set the Position of the Sun
to the Time and Date*

*(From March through November,
add an hour for Daylight Savings)*

Correction for Local Time _____

(Cut Out this Section Also)

I am   *Midnight*   *11 pm*

Orion Volvelle Horizon
(Orion Volvelle - Chapter 2)

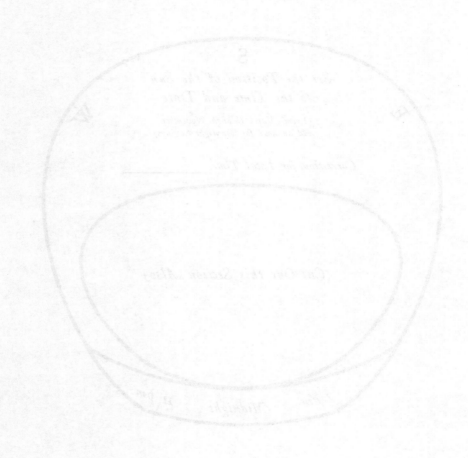

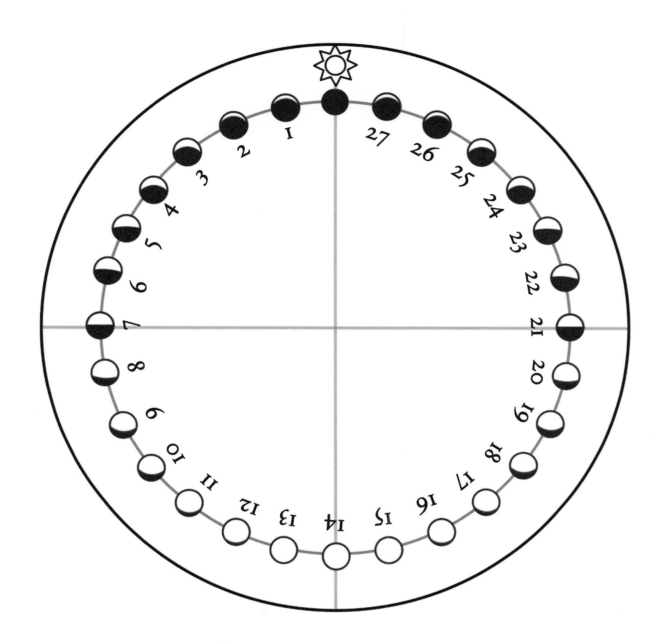

Moon Phase Wheel
(Sun-Moon Volvelle - Chapter 3)

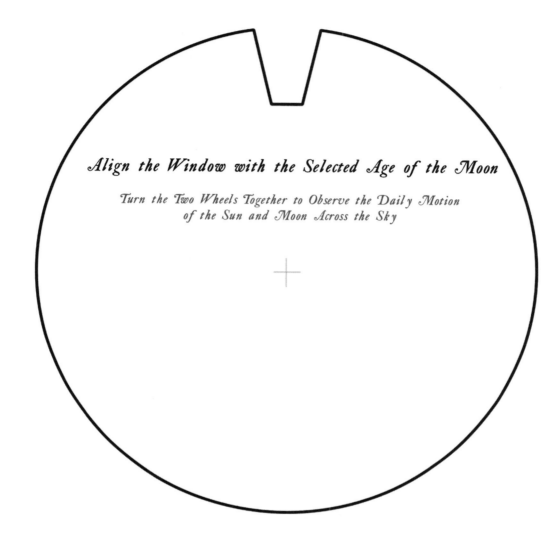

Align the Window with the Selected Age of the Moon

*Turn the Two Wheels Together to Observe the Daily Motion
of the Sun and Moon Across the Sky*

Window Wheel
(Sun-Moon Volvelle - Chapter 3)

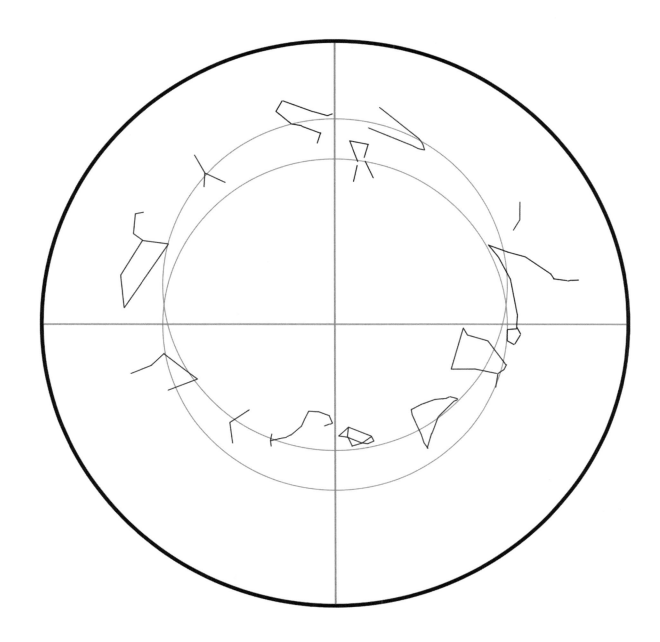

Zodiac Wheel
(Orion–Constellation Volvelle – Chapter 4)

Zodiac Wheel

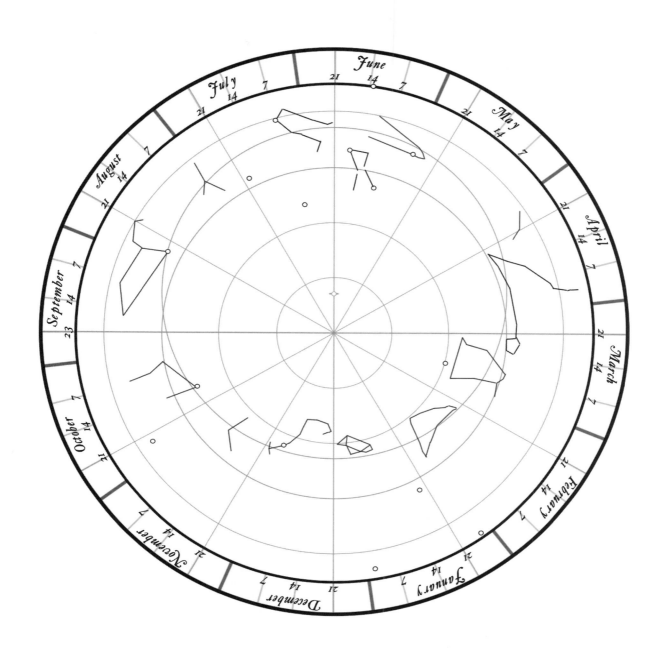

Constellation Wheel
(Orion-Constellation Volvelle - Chapter 5)

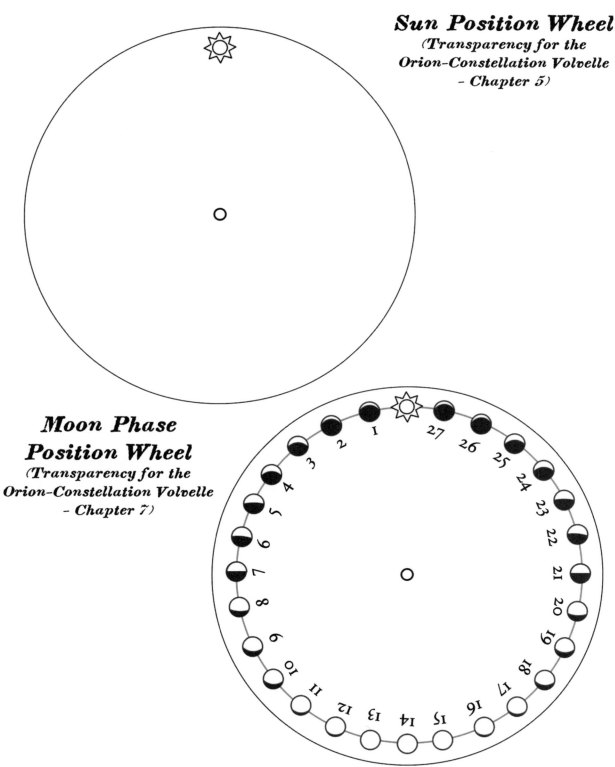

Sun Position Wheel
(Transparency for the Orion-Constellation Volvelle - Chapter 5)

Moon Phase Position Wheel
(Transparency for the Orion-Constellation Volvelle - Chapter 7)

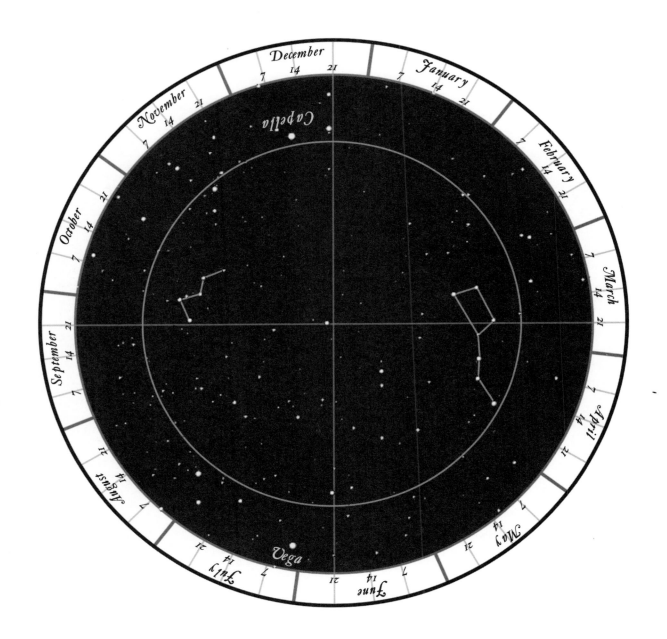

Northern Stars Wheel
(Northern Stars Volvelle - Chapter 6)

Permission is granted to the owner of the *Signs & Seasons* Workbook to make photocopies directly from this Volvelle Section of the Workbook for personal use. Copying of quantities for distribution or sale to others is expressly prohibited.

Northern Star's Wheel
Northern Star Points: Chapter 6

Test Manual

Testing Your Knowledge and Understanding of the Signs & Seasons Curriculum

The trying of your faith worketh patience. But let patience have her perfect work, that ye may be perfect and entire, wanting nothing - James 1:3b-4

Please Note:

To prepare for each test, the student should review the illustrations from the appropriate chapter of Signs & Seasons and understand the illustrated concepts. The tests will also measure the student's understanding of the terminology and associated concepts. Some questions require consulting the solar system maps and volvelles created for the respective chapters. Have these materials handy while taking the tests.

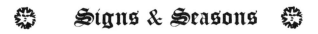

Test 1

Prologue – The Sky Above
Chapter 1 – The Light He Called Day

Write the term in the blank:

1. _____ The Greater Light that rules the day

2. _____ The Lesser Light that rules the night

3. _____ Collective name for the Two Great Lights

4. _____ Recognized patterns of stars

5. _____ The Biblical purpose for the Sun and Moon

6. _____ The shorter cycle of the Sun

7. _____ The cycle of the Moon

8. _____ The longer cycle of the Sun

9. _____ A system for measuring time by the cycles of the Sun and Moon

10. _____ A traditional resource with tables of astronomy information

11. _____ The basic unit for measuring the time from sunrise to sunrise

12. _____ The shorter intervals into which this basic unit is divided

13. _____ Number of these divisions that divide the basic unit

14. Label the two parts of the sundial and draw an arrow to show the direction travelled by the sundial shadows:

Write the term in the blank:

15. _____ Time when the Sun reaches the middle of the sky

16. _____ The imaginary line defining the middle of the sky

17. _____ Latin term for "before the middle of the day"

18. _____ Latin term for "after the middle of the day"

19. In the figure on the left, label the line in the middle of the sky and indicate at the proper places in the sky the letters that signify morning and afternoon:

20. Label the globe at right to name times represented by the sunshine and the shadow, and label the boundary between the sunlight and darkness:

Write the term in the blank:

21. _____ The time of darkness, when we pass within the Earth's shadow

22. _____ The transition period between sunlight and full darkness

23. _____ Direction toward the sunrise

24. _____ Direction toward the sunset

25. _____ Direction toward the Sun's highest point in the sky

26. _____ Direction away from the Sun's highest point in the sky

27. Label the directions on the compass of the globe at right:

Write the term in the blank:

28. _____ The circle of the limit of vision, where the edge of the Earth meets

    the sky

29. _____ The imaginary line around which the Earth rotates

30. Drawn an arrow and label to indicate the direction of Earth's rotation and the name of the line around which the Earth rotates:

31. Label the globes to correctly indicate the lines of sunrise and sunset:

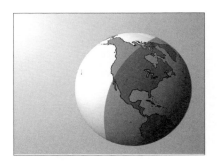

Test 2

Chapter 2 – The Darkness He Called Night

Write the term in the blank:

1. _____ A circular band of stars, seen only in dark, rural skies

2. _____ A man-made glow in the sky, caused by streetlights

3. _____ An informal grouping of stars, formed within a constellation

4. _____ The name of the North Star

5.   Label and connect the dots for the stars and constellations in the following figure:

The Big Dipper, the Little Dipper, Cassiopeia, the North Star, the "Pointers," Due North (indicated

on the horizon). *Hint - use a colored pencil or crayon to draw onto the dark areas*

6.   Label and connect the dots for the stars and constellations in the following figure:

Orion, Taurus, Sirius, and the Pleiades. *Hint - as above, use a colored pencil or crayon*

Write the term in the blank:

7.   _____ The Greek poet, our source for the traditional constellations

8.   _____ The "vault of the heavens" or "dome of the firmament"

9.   _____ A circle that divides a sphere into equal halves

10.   _____ A circle that divides a sphere into unequal sections

11.   Label the following: The axis, the celestial pole, the direction of Earth's rotation, the apparent direction of the rotation of the stars.

Write the term in the blank:

12. _____ The circle of stars that are always visible above the horizon

13. _____ The circle of stars that are never visible above the horizon

14. _____ The circle that defines the middle of the sky

15. _____ The directions where this circle crosses the horizon

16. _____ The point above the horizon directly overhead

17. _____ The point below the horizon directly underneath

18. Label the compass points on Earth and in the sky, label the circle that divides the sky into rising and setting halves and label the directions of each half.

Write the term in the blank:

19. _____ Circle that divides the sky into northern and southern halves.

20. _____ The famous constellation that lies on this circle.

21. _____ The directions where this circle crosses the horizon

22. Label the indicated parts on the traditional armillary sphere:

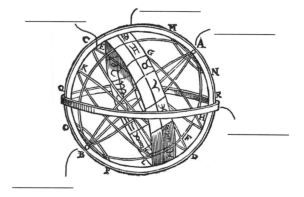

Test 3

Chapter 3 - The Cycle of the Month

1. Label the Moon's principal phases and quarters:

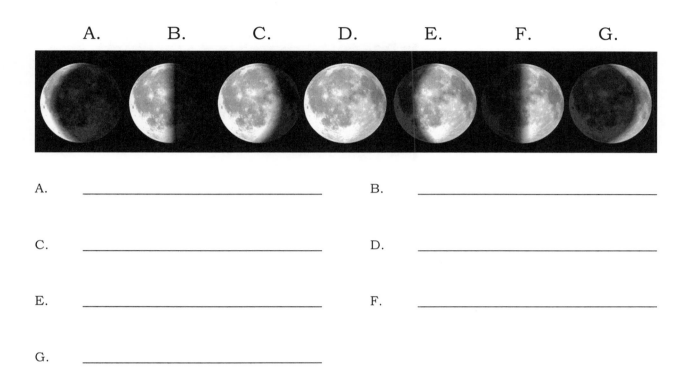

A. _____ B. _____

C. _____ D. _____

E. _____ F. _____

G. _____

2. For each Moon, shade in the shadows to indicate the progression of the phases. Indicate the direction the Moon moves in its orbit.

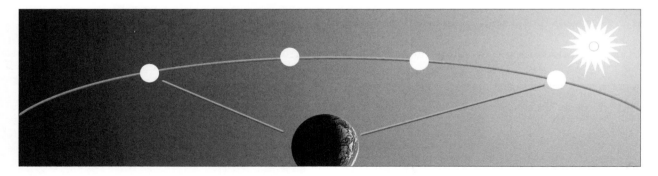

3. Shade in the shadows on the Moons to indicate the phases as seen after sunset over a four day period. Label the age of the Moon for each phase (Day 1, Day 2, etc).

Is the Moon waxing or waning? _____

4. Depict "earthshine" by drawing and labeling arrows that indicate the direction of light from its original source and reflected to the eye of the observer.

Write the answer in the blank:

5. _____ What is the average daily increase in the amount of time that the Moon rises after the Sun each day?

6. Shade in the Moon's shadows to show the phases as seen around sunset. Label the types of phases and indicate the daily motion of the Moon from night to night.

7.   Indicate and label the positions of the Full Moon at the following times: sunset, evening and midnight.   Show the direction that the Moon travels across the sky during this time.

Sunrise or sunset?

8.   _____ is when the waxing Moon can be seen.

9.   _____ is when the waning Moon can be seen.

10.   Shade in the shadows onto the Moons to indicate the phases as seen around sunrise. Label the types of phases and indicate the motion of the Moon from night to night.

11.   For each Moon, shade in the shadows to indicate the progression of the phases. Indicate the direction the Moon moves in its orbit.

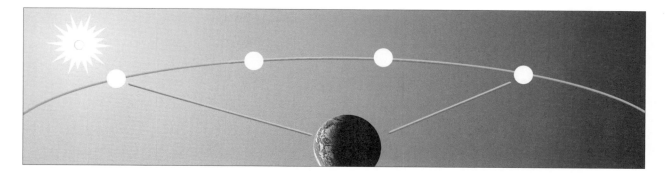

Write the average time of day when the Moon reaches the meridian at the following phases:

12. _____ New Moon

13. _____ First Quarter

14. _____ Full Moon

15. _____ Last Quarter

16.   Shade in the shadows on the Moons to indicate the phases as seen shortly before sunrise. Draw arrows to indicate the direction of Moon from morning to morning.

Write the answer in the blank:

17. _____ What is the average number of days in the lunar month, from one New Moon to the next.

Field Activity Questions

18.   Using your Moon phase volvelle, find the approximate time of day when the Moon crosses the meridian for the following days of the lunar month:

_____ Day 4   _____ Day 17

_____ Day 9   _____ Day 22

_____ Day 12   _____ Day 27

Test 4

Chapter 4 - The Tabernacle of the Sun

Write the answer in the blank:

1. _____ The annual cycle of light and dark and hot and cold

2. _____ The celestial event that occurs when the Moon crosses the ecliptic in proper alignment with the Sun

3. Draw arrows to indicate the direction of Earth in its orbit. On the outer circle, draw the apparent positions of the Sun in the sky as a result of the Earth's motion. Draw arrows to indicate the line of sight from the Earths to the Suns and the direction of the Sun's apparent movement. In what direction does the Sun appear to move? _____

Write the answer in the blank:

4. _____ Name the plane of the Earth's orbit

True or False?

5. _____ The zodiac is a band of constellations that lie along the plane of the solar system.

6. _____ The Sun, Moon, and planets appear to move through the constellations of the zodiac.

7. _____ The zodiac is a part of legitimate astronomy that has been appropriated by the superstition of astrology.

8. Label to indicate the name of the zodiac constellation and the object signified by this star pattern. (Bonus - indicate whether it is north, south, or on the celestial equator.)

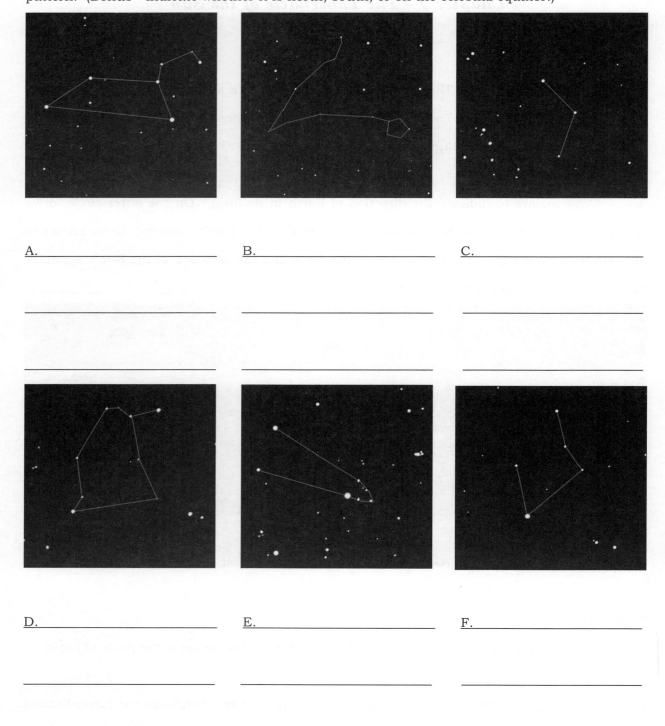

A._____   B._____   C._____

_____   _____   _____

_____   _____   _____

D._____   E._____   F._____

_____   _____   _____

_____   _____   _____

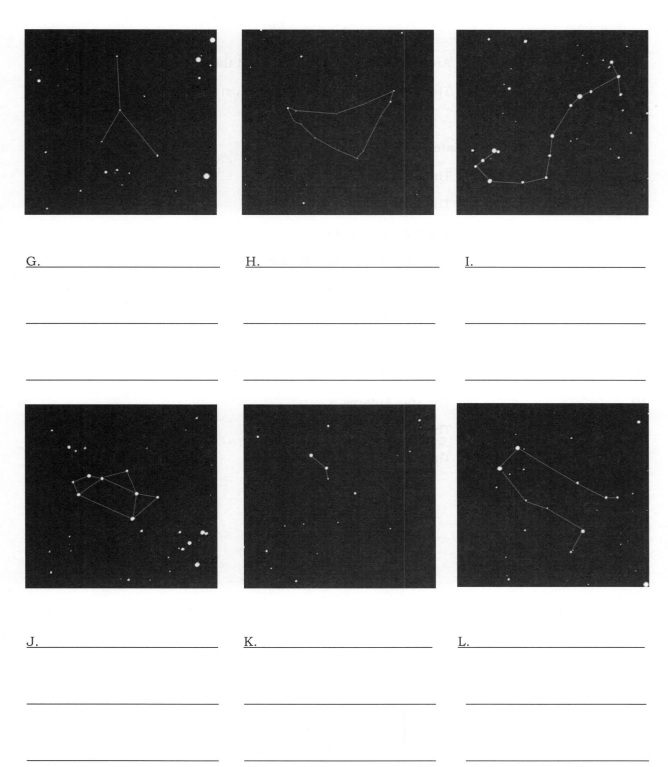

G. _____

_____

_____

H. _____

_____

_____

I. _____

_____

_____

J. _____

_____

_____

K. _____

_____

_____

L. _____

_____

_____

Write the answer in the blank:

9. _____ An intersection of the zodiac and the celestial equator

10. _____ The northernmost or southernmost extreme of the zodiac

Name the constellation associated with the following:

11. _____ The vernal equinox

12. _____ The Pleiades

13. _____ The star Aldebaran

14. _____ The stars Castor and Pollux

15. _____ The summer solstice

16. _____ The star Regulus

17. _____ The autumnal solstice

18. _____ The star Spica

19. _____ The star Antares

20. _____ The winter solstice

21. _____ The "teapot" asterism

Test 5

Chapter 5 – The Cycle of the Year

1. Draw an arrow and label to indicate the direction of the Sun's apparent motion along the ecliptic:

2. Label the seasons that begin when the Sun reaches these positions:

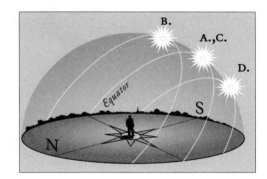

        A. _____

        B. _____

        C. _____

        D. _____

Write the answer in the blank:

3. The summer solstice is the _____ day of the year.

4. The winter solstice is the _____ day of the year.

5. On the equinoxes, the lengths of day and night are _____.

6. On the vernal equinox, the Sun heads in the direction _____ of the celestial equator.

7. On the autumnal equinox, the Sun heads in the direction _____ of the celestial equator.

8. _____ The zodiac constellation of the summer solstice.

9. The zodiac constellation of question #8 is _____ (farthest, closest) to the North Star.

10. _____ The zodiac constellation of the winter solstice.

11. The zodiac constellation of question #10 is _____ (farthest, closest) to the North Star.

12. _____ The zodiac constellation of the vernal equinox.

13. _____ The zodiac constellation of the autumnal equinox.

14. Label to indicate the sunrise positions on the equinoxes, the summer solstice, and the winter solstice:

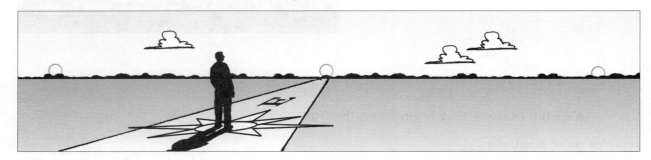

15. Label to indicate the sunset positions on the equinoxes, the summer solstice, and the winter solstice:

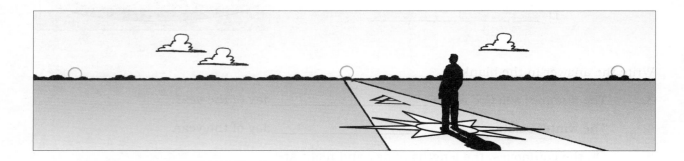

Write the indicated general direction:

16. _____ Where the Sun rises in late spring and early summer.

17. _____ Where the Sun sets in late spring and early summer.

18. _____ Where the Sun rises in late autumn and early winter.

19. _____ Where the Sun sets in late autumn and early winter.

20.   Name the months where the Sun is near its northern maximum and the days are longest:

A. _____

B. _____

C. _____

21.   Name the months where the Sun is near its southern maximum and the days are shortest:

A. _____

B. _____

C. _____

Write the answer in the blank:

22.   _____ The month generally the warmest for the northern hemisphere

23.   _____ The month generally the coldest for the northern hemisphere

24.   _____ Latitude where the day is 24 hours long on the summer solstice

25.   _____ Latitude where the Sun is directly overhead at noon on the summer solstice

Field Activity Questions

26.   Using your Orion-Zodiac volvelle, indicate the approximate times of day when the following constellations cross the meridian on the given dates

Date	Taurus	Leo	Scorpius	Aquarius
Vernal Equinox				
Summer Solstice				
Autumnal Equinox				
Winter Solstice				

Test 6
Chapter 6 – The Seasonal Skies

Name the constellation in which these first magnitude stars can be found:

1. _____ Aldebaran
2. _____ Sirius
3. _____ Betelgueuse
4. _____ Rigel
5. _____ Pollux
6. _____ Procyon
7. _____ Capella
8. _____ Regulus

9. _____ Spica
10. _____ Arcturus
11. _____ Vega
12. _____ Deneb
13. _____ Altair
14. _____ Antares
15. _____ Fomalhaut

16. Identify the first magnitude stars labeled by letters and the constellations labeled by numbers. Which season are these stars visible in the early evening? _____

A. _____
B. _____
C. _____
D. _____
E. _____
F. _____
G. _____

1. _____
2. _____
3. _____

4. _____
5. _____
6. _____

17.   Identify the first magnitude stars labeled by letters and the constellations labeled by numbers. Which season are these stars visible in the early evening? _____

A.   _____

B.   _____

C.   _____

1.   _____

2.   _____

3.   _____

4.   _____

5.   _____

18.   Identify the first magnitude stars labeled with numbers and constellations labeled with letters.

1.   _____

2.   _____

A.   _____

B.   _____

C.   _____

Bonus - write the rule that explains how these star patterns can be used to locate the bright stars 1. and 2. in the night sky.

_____

19.   Identify the first magnitude stars labeled by letters and the constellations labeled by numbers. Which season are these stars visible in the early evening?

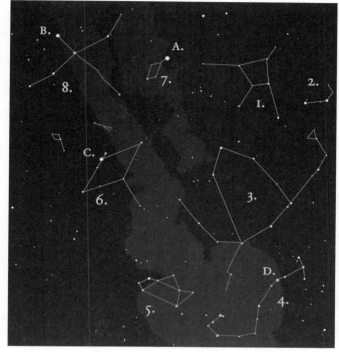

_____

A.   _____

B.   _____

C.   _____

D.   _____

1.   _____

2.   _____

3.   _____   6.   _____

4.   _____   7.   _____

5.   _____   8.   _____

20.   Identify the first magnitude stars labeled by letters and the constellations labeled by numbers. Which season are these stars visible in the early evening?

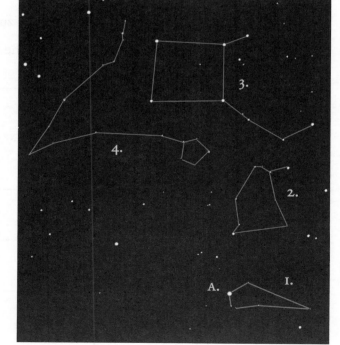

_____

A.   _____

1.   _____

2.   _____

3.   _____

4.   _____

Name the terms:

21. _____ The first appearance of star before the sunrise

22. _____ When a star rises visibly in the night sky

23. _____ The invisible rising of a star during the daytime

24. Write the approximate time of day (sunrise, sunset, noon or midnight) when the Big Dipper is east of Polaris for each season:

A. _____ early spring   B. _____ early summer

C. _____ early autumn   D. _____ early winter

25. Write the approximate time of day (sunrise, sunset, noon or midnight) when Orion is near the meridian for each season:

A. _____ early spring   B. _____ early summer

C. _____ early autumn   D. _____ early winter

Field Activity Questions

26. Using your solar system maps, list the zodiac constellation hosting the Sun and the zodiac constellations rising as the Sun sets for the following months:

Month	The Sun is in...	The constellation Rising at Sunset
April		
July		
October		
January		

27. Using your Orion-Zodiac volvelle, list the approximate times of day when the following first magnitude stars are near the meridian in the middle of the following months:

Star	February	May	August	November
Arcturus				
Betelgueuse				
Vega				
Rigel				
Pollux				
Fomalhaut				
Regulus				

28. Using your Northern Sky volvelle, list the approximate times of day when Capella and Vega are "balanced" during the following months:

Month	Capella west, Vega east	Vega west, Capella east
February		
May		
August		
November		

Test 7
Chapter 7 – The Wandering Stars

List the name of the classical planet for each of the descriptive Greek names:

1. _____ Phainon, "The Shining Star"

2. _____ Phosphoros, "The Light Bearer"

3. _____ Pyrois, "The Fiery Star"

4. _____ Stilbon, "The Gleaming Star"

5. _____ Phaethon, "The Bright Star"

6. List the inferior planets _____

7. List the classical superior planets _____

8. List the modern planets _____

Give the term for the definition:

9. _____ A close approach of two celestial bodies lined up in the sky

10. _____ When a planet is on the far side of the Sun from Earth

11. _____ A planet's apparent separation from the Sun

12. _____ A planet's greatest apparent separation from the Sun

13. _____ A pause in a planet's motion before changing direction

14. _____ When an inferior planet is between the Earth and the Sun

15. _____ When a planet is one-quarter of the zodiac circle from the Sun

16. _____ When a superior planet rises opposite from the Sun

17. Name the directions of the elongations of an inferior planet for the indicated time of day.

A. A planet at _____ elongation is visible around sunset.

B. A planet at _____ elongation is visible around sunrise.

18.   Write the seasons corresponding to these quarters of the Moon:

A. _____   B. _____   C. _____

D. _____   E. _____   F. _____

G. _____   H. _____   I. _____

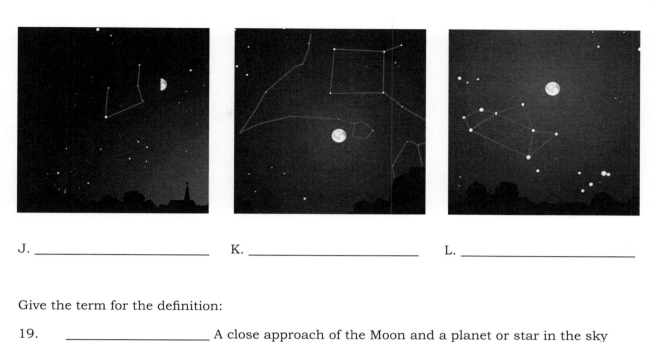

J. _____ K. _____ L. _____

Give the term for the definition:

19. _____ A close approach of the Moon and a planet or star in the sky

20. _____ A close approach of a planet with a star or another planet

21. _____ A close approach where the Moon covers a star or planet

Field Activity Questions

22.   Using your Orion-Zodiac volvelle, for each month indicated, list the approximate age of the Moon (i.e. the day of the lunar month) when the Moon passes near the following ecliptic stars:

Star	February	May	August	November
Aldebaran				
Spica				
Pollux				
Antares				
Regulus				

Test 8
Epilogue – The Calendar

Write the answer in the blank:

1. _____ An extra month or day added to make a calendar agree with celestial cycles

2. _____ The nation that developed the first solar calendar

3. _____ The first solar calendar was based on this star's heliacal rising

4. _____ This heliacal rising coincided with the flood of this river

5. _____ The inventor of the Julian calendar

6. _____ In the Julian calendar, the number of years between leap years

7. _____ The number of years in the cycle of the Jewish calendar

8. _____ The Hebrew name for Passover

9. _____ The Moon phase of Passover

10. _____ The Greek name of Passover, used in most European languages instead of "Easter"

11. _____ The church council that established the rule for finding the date for celebrating Easter

12. _____ The number of leap year days omitted every 400 years in the Gregorian calendar

13. _____ Type of clock used today as the standard timekeeper

Find the date of Easter given the following circumstances:

14. _____ The Full Moon is on Thursday, April 10.

15. _____ The vernal equinox is on a Tuesday, and the First Quarter Moon is two days later.

16. _____ The equinox is on a Saturday, and the Moon is twenty-five days old.

- 151 -

17. _____ The equinox is on a Sunday, and the Full Moon is the day after. What is the date of Easter?

18. _____ The equinox is on a Sunday, and the Full Moon is the day before. What is the date of Easter?

19. _____ The equinox is on a Monday, and the old Moon is two days before New. What is the date of Easter?

20. Use the Gregorian leap year rule to determine whether the following years would be leap years. (Write Yes or No):

A. _____ 2004   B. _____ 1990   C. _____ 1900

D. _____ 1776   E. _____ 1620   F. _____ 1812

G. _____ 2000   H. _____ 1800   I. _____ 1980

J. _____ 1582   K. _____ 1600   L. _____ 1752

Answer Key

Correct Anſwers to the Chapter Teſts and Guidelines for Aſſigning a Letter Grade for the Signs & Seaſons Courſe

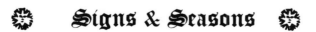

Instructions

The Tests in this Manual are intended to cover the most significant aspects of the subject matter in *Signs & Seasons*. However, there are varying degrees of complexity to the topics, and some may be more familiar to the student or easier to grasp than others. For example, the elementary "day and night" subject matter of Chapter 1 may be easier for the student than the more advanced "seasonal" topics of Chapters 5 and 6. Also, a student's ability to observe and identify constellations will vary upon whether the family lives under dark rural skies or the washed out skies of the city.

Variable Point Value

For these reasons, a higher point value is assigned to questions deemed to be more essential to the overall goals and purposes of the course, namely, to impart an understanding of the observables associated with timekpeeing and navigation. Most of the tests include a number of extra bonus points to accommodate more complex subject matter and the various circumstances of different students. The bonus point value for each test varies. A greater number of bonus points are included on some tests to allow latitude for topic areas deemed to be more difficult.

Cumulative Scoring

The subject matter of the tests is cumulative, and thus the later tests require a grasp of the earlier subject matter. Therefore, the student is responsible for understanding the chapters previous to each test, and a final grade will be assigned based on the total point value of all tests.

How to Grade the Tests

In the Answer Key, a blank is provided next to each correct answer. To score credit, simply make a check mark next to each correct answer. For answers worth more than one point, write the number of points for each correct answer. Use your judgement in assigning partial credit if an answer is close but not entirely correct. At the end, simply add up the number of correct points for the test and write this number in the "total points" space. If parents wish to give a letter grade for the test, divide the total correct points by the number indicated for each test. The parents may use their own judgement in further modifying the tests or point values.

Flexible Timetable

There is no particular timetable for completing the tests. However it is highly recommended that some or all of the Field Activities for each chapter be performed before testing that chapter. Since some of these Field Activities include recording measurements over a period of weeks and months, it may not be necessary to wait for completion of each series of observations before testing. However, the student should at least observe the trends of the observations and possess a comfortable understanding of the phenomena.

Student Preparation for Tests

The chapters in *Signs & Seasons* are short and heavily illustrated, so the students should review the illustrations before taking the tests. Some tests include questions that use the star maps and volvelles created in the field activities for each chapter. The students should complete these activities before taking the test for that chapter, and have those materials available while taking the test.

Test 1 - Answers

Prologue - The Sky Above
Chapter 1 - The Light He Called Day

(Terminology - two points each)

1. _____ The Sun

2. _____ The Moon

3. _____ The Luminaries

4. _____ Constellation

5. _____ Timekeeping, or "signs and seasons, and days and years"

6. _____ The Day

7. _____ The Month

8. _____ The Year

9. _____ Calendar

10. _____ Almanack

11. _____ The Day

12. _____ The Hour

13. _____ 24

(Sundial Figure - six points total)

14. _____

gnomon

dial

(Terminology - two points each)

15. _____ Noon

16. _____ The Meridian

17. _____ Ante Meridiem

18. _____ Post Meridiem

(For the following figures, score twelve points each (four for each indicated element))

19. _____

20. _____

(Terminology - two points each)

21. _____ Night

22. _____ Twilight

23. _____ East

24. _____ West

25. _____ South

26. _____ North

(Compass Globe Figure - eight points total)

27. _____

(Terminology - two points each)

28. _____ The Horizon

29. _____ The Axis

(Rotating Earth Figure - six points total)

30. _____

(Sunrise and Sunset - six points total for both)

31. _____

_____

Total Points (out of 100)

Test 2 – Answers

Chapter 2 – The Darkness He Called Night

(Terminology - one point each)

1. _____ The Milky Way

2. _____ Light Pollution

3. _____ Asterism

4. _____ Polaris

(Northern Sky Figure - very important foundational topic - 27 points total (score three points for each of the nine indicated elements - six labels, three "connect the dot" patterns)

5. _____

(Orion Sky Figure - very important foundational topic - 18 points total (score three points for each of the six indicated elements - four labels, two "connect the dot" patterns)

6. _____

(Terminology - one point each)

7. _____ Aratus

8. _____ Celestial Sphere

9. _____ Great Circle

10. _____ Small Circle

(Rotation Figure - important foundational topic - 12 points total (score three points for each of the four indicated elements)

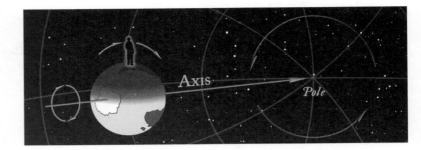

11.   _____

(Terminology - one point each)

12.   _____ Northern Circumpolar Circle or Arctic Circle

13.   _____ Southern Circumpolar Circle

14.   _____ The Meridian

15.   _____ North and South (score one point each)

16.   _____ The Zenith

17.   _____ The Nadir

(Direction Figure - important topic - 22 points total (score two points for each of the eleven indicated elements)

18.   _____

(Terminology - one point each)

19.   _____ Celestial Equator

20.   _____ Orion

21.   _____ East and West (score one point each)

(Armillary - five points total)

22.   _____

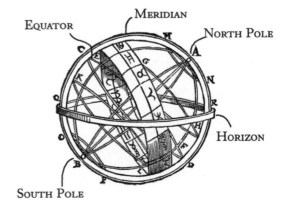

_____

Total Points (out of 100, test includes one bonus point)

1. (Moon's Principal Phases - one point each)

A. _____ Waning Crescent

B. _____ Last Quarter

C. _____ Waning Gibbous

D. _____ Full Moon

E. _____ Waxing Gibbous

F. _____ First Quarter

G. _____ Waxing Crescent

(Moon phase progression - five points total, score one for each correct element (four shaded phases, one direction arrow))

2. _____

(Waxing crescent - eight points total, score one for each correct element (four shaded phases, four labels)

3. _____

(Waxing or waning - one point)

_____ Waxing

(Earthshine - six points total, score one for each

correct arrow and label)

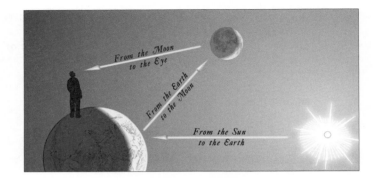

4. _____

(Question - one point)

5. _____ 48 minutes

(Waxing phases - 32 points total, score two points for each of the correct element (shaded phases, labels, and arrows))

6. _____

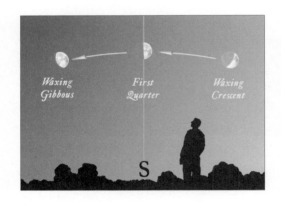

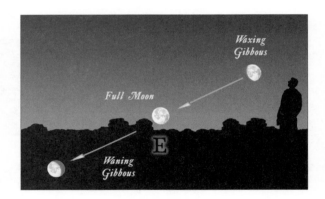

(Full Moon - five points, score one for each element (labels

and arrows))

7. _____

(Questions - one point each)

8. _____ Sunset

9. _____ Sunrise

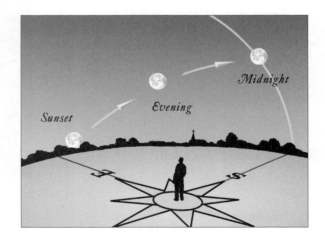

(Waning phases - sixteen total, score two points for each of the correct element (shaded phases, labels, and arrows))

10. _____

(Moon phase progression - five points total, score one for each correct element (four shaded phases, one direction arrow))

11. _____

(Times of day (score one point each)

12. _____ Noon

13. _____ Evening (Sunset)

14. _____ Midnight

15. _____ Morning (Sunrise)

(Waning crescent - seven points total, score one for each correct element (four shaded phases, three arrows))

16. _____

(Question and volvelle - one point each)

17. _____ 29.5 days   18.   *Answers may vary depending on the ease of reading the volvelle*

Day 4 _____ between 3:00 and 3:30 PM   Day 17 _____ between 2:30 and 3:00 AM

Day 9 _____ between 3:00 and 3:30 PM   Day 22 _____ between 6:30 and 7:00 AM

Day 12 _____ between 10:00 and 10:30 PM   Day 27 _____ between 11:00 and 11:30 AM

_____

Total Points (out of 100, test includes seven bonus points)

Test 4 – Answers

Chapter 4 – The Tabernacle of the Sun

(Terminology - one point each)

1. _____ The Seasons

2. _____ Eclipse

(Sun motion - seven points total, score one for each of the three Sun positions, one for each "line of sight" arrow, and one for indicating the direction of the Sun's apparent movement)

3. _____

(Question - One point)

_____ East

(Terminology, True or False - one point each)

4. _____ Ecliptic

5. _____ True

6. _____ True

7. _____ True

8. (Constellation identification - important foundational topic - 60 points total - for each constellation, score two points each for the constellation name and the object signified by the constellation. Bonus - score one point for indicating whether the constellation is north, south, or on the celestial equator. Review the images in Chapter 4 for more information)

A.	_____ Leo	Lion	North of the celestial equator
B.	_____ Pisces	Fishes	North of the celestial equator
C.	_____ Libra	Balance	South of the celestial equator
D.	_____ Aquarius	Waterbearer	On the celestial equator
E.	_____ Taurus	Bull	North of the celestial equator
F.	_____ Virgo	Maiden	On the celestial equator

G.	_____ Cancer	Crab	North of the celestial equator
H.	_____ Capricornus	Goat	South of the celestial equator
I.	_____ Scorpius	Scorpoin	South of the celestial equator
J.	_____ Sagittarius	Archer	South of the celestial equator
K.	_____ Aries	Ram	North of the celestial equator
L.	_____ Gemini	Twins	North of the celestial equator

(Important Terminology and constellation names - score three points each)

9.   _____ Equinox

10.   _____ Solstice

11.   _____ Pisces

12.   _____ Taurus

13.   _____ Taurus

14.   _____ Gemini

15.   _____ Gemini

16.   _____ Leo

17.   _____ Virgo

18.   _____ Virgo

19.   _____ Scorpius

20.   _____ Sagittarius

21.   _____ Sagittarius

_____

Total Points (out of 100, test includes thirteen bonus points)

Test 5 - Answers

Chapter 5 - The Cycle of the Year

(Sun apparent motion - four points total, score two for an arrow of the Sun's apparent direction and two for labelling as "East")

1. _____

(Seasonal signposts - score two points each)

2 A. _____ Spring or Autumn

  B. _____ Summer

  C. _____ Spring or Autumn

  D. _____ Winter

(Fill in the blanks - foundational topics - score two points each)

3. _____ Longest

4. _____ Shortest

5. _____ Equal

6. _____ North

7. _____ South

8. _____ Gemini

9. _____ Closest

10. _____ Sagittarius

11. _____ Farthest

12. _____ Pisces

13. _____ Virgo

(Sunrise positions - six points total, score two each correctly labeled sunrise)

14. _____

(Sunset positions - six points total, score two each correctly labeled sunset)

15. _____

(Fill in the blanks - two points each)

16. _____ Northeast

17. _____ Northwest

18. _____ Southeast

19. _____ Southwest

(Sun's northern and southern maximums - two points each)

20. A. _____ July

   B. _____ June

   C. _____ May

21. A. _____ January

   B. _____ December

   C. _____ November

(Fill in the blanks - two points each)

22. _____ August

23. _____ February

24. _____ Arctic Circle (66 1/2 degrees North)

25. _____ Tropic of Cancer (23 1/2 degress North)

(Volvelle table - 32 points total, score two points for each. Give credit if the indicated answers are within an hour - give or take. Volvelles are not precise and there can be variability due to imperfections in the volvelle, interpretation of the instructions, and corrections for standard time and daylight savings. This portion of the test is intended to judge general competence at using and interpreting the volvelle so additional consideration should be taken in grading.)

26.

Date	*Taurus*	*Leo*	*Scorpius*	*Aquarius*
Vernal Equinox	6:00 PM	12:00 PM	6:00 AM	12:00 AM
Summer Solstice	12:00 AM	6:00 PM	12:00 PM	6:00 AM
Autumnal Equinox	6:00 AM	12:00 AM	6:00 PM	12:00 PM
Winter Solstice	11:00 PM	5:00 AM	11:00 AM	5:00 PM

_____ Points for this table

_____

Total Points (out of 100, test includes six bonus points)

Test 6 - Answers

Chapter 6 - The Seasonal Skies

(Constellation identification - 15 points total - for each constellation, score one point each for the constellation name.)

1. _____ Taurus
2. _____ Canis Major or Big Dog
3. _____ Orion
4. _____ Orion
5. _____ Gemini
6. _____ Canis Minor or Little Dog
7. _____ Auriga
8. _____ Leo

9. _____ Virgo
10. _____ Boötes
11. _____ Lyra
12. _____ Cygnus
13. _____ Aquila
14. _____ Scorpius
15. _____ Piscis Austrinis or Southern Fish

_____ Total this section (of 15)

(Star and constellation identification - score one point each for each star and constellation name and also the season for each sky (problems 16-20). Note - five point bonus question included with problem 18.)

16. _____ Winter

A. _____ Sirius
B. _____ Betelgeuse
C. _____ Rigel
D. _____ Procyon
E. _____ Pollux
F. _____ Aldebaran
G. _____ Capella

1. _____ Orion
2. _____ Canis Major or Big Dog
3. _____ Canis Minor or Little Dog
4. _____ Gemini
5. _____ Taurus
6. _____ Auriga

_____ Total this section (of 14)

17. _____ Spring

A. _____ Regulus   1. _____ Leo

B. _____ Spica   2. _____ Virgo

C. _____ Arcturus   3. _____ Corvus

                              4. _____ Gemini

                              5. _____ Libra

                              6. _____ Boötes

_____ Total this section (of 10)

18.

1. _____ Arcturus   A. _____ Big Dipper or Ursa Major

2. _____ Spica   B. _____ Boötes

                              C. _____ Virgo

Q?. _____ Follow the "arc" to Arcturus and follow the "spike" to Spica (five points)

_____ Total this section (of 10)

19. _____ Summer

A. _____ Vega   1. _____ Hercules

B. _____ Deneb   2. _____ Corona Borealis or Northern Crown

C. _____ Altair   3. _____ Ophiuchus

D. _____ Antares   4. _____ Scorpius

                              5. _____ Sagittarius

                              6. _____ Aquila

                              7. _____ Lyra

                              8. _____ Cygnus

_____ Total this section (of 13)

20. _____ Autumn

A. _____ Fomalhaut

1. _____ Piscis Austrinis

2. _____ Aquarius

3. _____ Pegasus

4. _____ Pisces

_____ Total this section (of 6)

(Terminology - score one point each)

21. _____ Heliacal rising

22. _____ Temporal rising

23. _____ Cosmic rising

(Seasonal constellations - score one point each)

24. A. _____ Sunset   25. A. _____ Sunset

    B. _____ Noon   B. _____ Noon

    C. _____ Sunrise   C. _____ Sunrise

    D. _____ Midnight   D. _____ Midnight

_____ Total this section (of 8)

(Solar Map Table - eight points total - score one point for each correct answer)

Month	*The Sun is in...*	*The constellation Rising at Sunset*
April	Aries	Libra
July	Cancer	Capricornus
October	Libra	Aries
January	Capricornus	Cancer

_____ Points for this table

(Volvelle tables - score one point for each. Give credit if the indicated answers are within an hour - give or take. Volvelles are not precise and there can be variability due to imperfections in the volvelle, interpretation of the instructions, and corrections for standard time and daylight savings. This portion of the test is intended to judge general competence at using and interpreting the volvelle so additional consideration should be taken in grading.)

26.   Orion-Zodiac volvelle - Times of stars at the meridian (28 points total)

Star	February	May	August	November
Arcturus	4:30 AM	11:30 PM	5:30 PM	11:30 AM
Betelgueuse	8:15 PM	3:15 PM	9:15 AM	3:15 AM
Vega	9:00 AM	4:00 AM	10:00 PM	4:00 PM
Rigel	7:30 PM	2:30 PM	8:30 AM	2:30 AM
Pollux	10:00 PM	5:00 PM	11:00 AM	5:00 AM
Fomalhaut	1:00 PM	8:00 AM	2:00 AM	8:00 PM
Regulus	12:30 AM	7:30 PM	1:30 PM	7:30 AM

_____ Points for this table

27.   Northern Sky volvelle - Times when Capella and Vega are "balanced" (eight points total)

Month	Capella west, Vega east	Vega west, Capella east
February	2:30 AM	2:00 PM
May	9:30 PM	9:00 AM
August	3:30 PM	3:00 AM
November	9:30 AM	9:00 PM

_____ Points for this table

_____

Total Points (out of 100, test includes twenty-three bonus points)

Test 7 – Answers

Chapter 7 – The Wandering Stars

(Greek planet names - score one point each)

1. _____ Saturn

2. _____ Venus

3. _____ Mars

4. _____ Mercury

5. _____ Jupiter

(Planet lists - score two points for each correct answer)

6. _____ Mercury, Venus (four points total)

7. _____ Mars, Jupiter, Saturn (six points total)

8. _____ Uranus, Neptune (four points total - minus one point for including Pluto)

(Important Terminology - score two points each)

9. _____ Conjunction

10. _____ Superior Conjunction

11. _____ Elongation

12. _____ Maximum Elongation

13. _____ Station

14. _____ Inferior Conjunction

15. _____ Quadrature

16. _____ Opposition

17. Elongations of inferior planets - score two points each for each correct answer

A. _____ Eastern Elongation

B. _____ Western Elongation

(Seasonal Moon quarters - important indicator of cumulative understanding of the subject matter - score three points for each correct answer (36 points total))

18.

A. _____ Autumn   B. _____ Winter   C. _____ Spring

D. _____ Spring   E. _____ Winter   F. _____ Summer

G. _____ Autumn   H. _____ Winter   I. _____ Spring

J. _____ Summer   K. _____ Autumn   L. _____ Summer

_____ Points for this section

(Important Terminology - score two points each)

19. _____ Lunar Conjunction

20. _____ Planetary Conjunction

21. _____ Occultation

(Volvelle table - score two points for each. Give credit if the indicated answers are within two days - give or take. As mentioned previously, volvelles are not precise and there can be much variability in construction and interpretation. This portion of the test is intended to judge general competence at using and interpreting the volvelle so additional consideration should be taken in grading.)

22.   Orion-Zodiac volvelle - Approximate age of the Moon for lunar conjunctions (40 points total)

Star	February	May	August	November
Aldebaran	8 days	1 day	21 days	14 days
Spica	20 days	13 days	5 days	26 days
Pollux	12 days	5 days	25 days	18 days
Antares	23 days	16 days	8 days	1 day
Regulus	16 days	9 days	1 day	22 days

_____ Points for this table

_____

Total Points (out of 100, this test includes twenty-one bonus points)

Test 8 – Answers

Epilogue – The Calendar

(Important Terminology - score three points each)

1. _____ intercalary or intercalation

2. _____ Egypt

3. _____ Sirius

4. _____ The Nile

5. _____ Julius Caesar

6. _____ Four years

7. _____ Nineteen years

8. _____ Pesach

9. _____ Full Moon or "the fourteenth day"

10. _____ Pascha

11. _____ Council of Nicaea

12. _____ Three days

13. _____ Atomic clock

(Dates of Easter following the rule - These problems indicate a cumulative understanding of all the subject matter presented in Signs & Seasons - score four points each (24 points total for this section. Note - some calculations can vary by one day depending on "full" or "hollow" months)

14. _____ April 13

15. _____ April 3

16. _____ April 11 or 12

17. _____ March 28

18. _____ April 17 or 18

19. _____ April 6

(Gregorian Leap Years - These problems also indicate a cumulative understanding of all the subject matter - score four
points each)

20.   A.   _____ 2004 - YES

       B.   _____ 1990 - NO

       C.   _____ 1900 - NO

       D.   _____ 1776 - YES

       E.   _____ 1620 - YES

       F.   _____ 1812 - YES

       G.   _____ 2000 - YES

       H.   _____ 1800 - NO

       I.   _____ 1980 - YES

       J.   _____ 1582 - YES

       K.   _____ 1600 - YES

       L.   _____ 1752 - YES

_____

Total Points (out of 100, this test includes eleven bonus points)

Final Grade
Cumulative Based on all the Test Scores

Test 1   _____ Total Points (out of 100)

Test 2   _____ Total Points (out of 100)

Test 3   _____ Total Points (out of 100)

Test 4   _____ Total Points (out of 100)

Test 5   _____ Total Points (out of 100)

Test 6   _____ Total Points (out of 100)

Test 7   _____ Total Points (out of 100)

Test 8   _____ Total Points (out of 100)

_____ Grand Total (out of 800)

_____ % - Percentage Score (Grand Total divided by 800 points)

Grade Scale	
93 - 100%	A
85 - 92%	B
77 - 84%	C
70 - 76%	D
0 - 69%	F

(Note - if appropriate, please substitute a different scale suitable to your jurisdiction)

_____ Course Grade

Notes